Illuminating the Path

Illuminating the Path

James J. Thomas and Kristin A. Cook, Editors

IEEE
COMPUTER
SOCIETY

Trademarks

Published 2005
Printed by IEEE in the United States of America
ISBN 0-7695-2323-4

Library of Congress Control Number: 2005929723

Additional Copies of This Book

Additional copies of this book may be ordered from the IEEE Computer Society:

IEEE Computer Society Order Number: R0230

IEEE Computer Society
Customer Service Center
10662 Los Vaqueros Circle
Los Alamitos, California 90720 USA
Tel (toll-free): +1 800 CS BOOKS
Tel (direct): +1 714 821 8380
Fax: +1 714 821 4641
E-mail: csbooks@computer.org
Website: http://www.computer.org/portal/page/store/catalog/r0230.html

Preface

The threat of terrorism in our homeland became horrifically real on September 11, 2001. The shock was felt at home and around the world. The subsequent response to this threat has taken many forms, including the development of new technologies intended to provide a technical advantage that can aid in thwarting terrorism.

One important area for technical advancement is the development of advanced information technologies to support the homeland security mission. For centuries we have been improving our ability to collect information, and this will continue. However, our ability to analyze this information is sorely lacking. The information is massive, complex, incomplete, and uncertain, and it encompasses all data forms, languages, and cultures. Technologies are needed that will support the application of human judgment to make the best possible use of this information and share it with others as appropriate to prevent, deter, and respond to threats.

The US Department of Homeland Security (DHS) chartered the National Visualization and Analytics Center™ (NVAC™) in 2004 with the goal of helping to counter future terrorist attacks in the United States and around the globe. A major objective for NVAC is to define a long-term research and development (R&D) agenda for visual analytics to address the most pressing needs in R&D to facilitate advanced analytical insight.

Under the leadership of the Pacific Northwest National Laboratory (PNNL), the R&D agenda for visual analytics was developed to define the directions and priorities for future R&D programs focused on visual analytics tools. This agenda, *Illuminating the Path*, provides a coordinated technical vision for government and industrial investments and helps ensure that a continual stream of technology and tools enter the hands of analysts and emergency responders.

Agenda Development Process

Development of the visual analytics agenda began after a survey of leading universities' researchers found that traditional views of the needed sciences, such as visualization, did not address the required capabilities. We needed to achieve a broad understanding of the requirements in order to enable the best talents to address the technical challenges. Achieving this understanding required training from those dealing with border protection, emergency response, and analysis. It also required the assembly of a dedicated team of highly motivated people to develop this agenda.

We placed an open call for leaders in many fields to participate by submitting short white papers and biographies. The response was overwhelming in terms of both the quality and quantity of submittals. The NVAC Advisory Board, composed of representatives from industry, academia, government, and national laboratories, had the difficult job of selecting about 25 representative leaders.

The selected scientists, analysts, and applied mission experts were challenged to develop this agenda within 9 months for its sponsor, DHS. To accomplish this, the panel met twice for 3-day structured workshops. During both workshops, about half the time was devoted to training by experienced instructors educating the scientific community on the user community's needs. This training changed many views of the panel members about the technological advancements needed to support the homeland security mission. Our instructors fully participated in the workshops to provide their guidance to the team.

Key topics were selected and organized into chapters; chapter leads and authors volunteered to develop the content; and drafts of the agenda were iteratively produced, reviewed, and edited. The product is documented in this book.

The R&D agenda described herein is only a beginning. It constitutes a grand challenge for the scientific enterprise, but more importantly, achieving the agenda is vital to the mission to protect our homeland. As you read this book, we encourage you to think carefully about the role you can play in advancing the science of visual analytics toward helping to safeguard our nation.

Acknowledgments

We must first express our appreciation to DHS for their sponsorship of this effort, particularly Joseph Kielman, Maureen McCarthy, Alexandra Landsberg, and David Shepherd. Their unwavering support and guidance have been essential to this process.

We would like to personally thank the many authors and contributors who dedicated their time and effort to the development of this R&D agenda. We would especially like to acknowledge the following individuals who acted as advisors on the creation of this book. We deeply appreciate their hard work, diligence, and perseverance on the many and complicated editorial aspects of this project. Their efforts enabled the completion of this book within a very short timeframe. Without their passion and drive, this book would not have been possible.

Nancy Chinchor	Central Intelligence Agency
Pat Hanrahan	Stanford University
George Robertson	Microsoft Corporation
Russ Rose	Central Intelligence Agency

We are sincerely grateful to the members of the R&D agenda panel. These individuals were selected in 2004 as the best and brightest multidisciplinary team to define this agenda. The panel members' individual technical strengths were applied in writing the agenda. The team made many personal sacrifices to see this project to completion. We are honored to have these great individuals as part of the agenda development and author team.

Anthony Bartoletti	Lawrence Livermore National Laboratory
Mark Billinghurst	Human Interface Technology Laboratory, New Zealand
Stuart Card	Palo Alto Research Center
Dan Carr	George Mason University
John Dill	Simon Fraser University
Rae Earnshaw	University of Bradford, UK
Dave Ebert	Purdue University
Stephen Eick	University of Illinois, Chicago and SSS Research

Robert Grossman	University of Illinois, Chicago
Chuck Hansen	University of Utah
Don Jones	Pacific Northwest National Laboratory
Ken Joy	University of California, Davis
David Kasik	The Boeing Company
David Laidlaw	Brown University
Sharon Laskowski	National Institute of Standards and Technology
Alan MacEachren	The Pennsylvania State University
Catherine Plaisant	University of Maryland
Bill Ribarsky	University of North Carolina, Charlotte
John Stasko	Georgia Institute of Technology
Maureen Stone	Stone Soup Consulting
Alan Turner	Pacific Northwest National Laboratory
Matt Ward	Worcester Polytechnic Institute
David White	Sandia National Laboratory
Pak Chung Wong	Pacific Northwest National Laboratory
David Woods	The Ohio State University
Bill Wright	Oculus Info, Inc.

In addition to the panel members, several other individual authors worked on the agenda. They all brought their unique perspective and technical background to this project. We are thankful for each of their contributions.

Brian Fisher	University of British Columbia
Beth Hetzler	Pacific Northwest National Laboratory
Donna Peuquet	The Pennsylvania State University
Mark Whiting	Pacific Northwest National Laboratory
Paul Whitney	Pacific Northwest National Laboratory

We are also grateful for the participation and advice of Lucy Nowell of the Advanced Research and Development Activity. Lucy provided a valuable government perspective to the workshops.

Setting the context for the complexity and magnitude of problems faced by analysts and first responders required significant training by several intelligence community resources. We are especially grateful to David Moore from the National Security Agency and Frank Hughes from the Joint Military Intelligence College, who acted as consultants to the panel. Their training enabled a deep understanding of the need for visual analytics technologies to combat terrorism.

We also thank those individuals who contributed countless hours to the production of this book. Our sincere appreciation goes to Jill Farris, NVAC's Operations Manager, for her efforts in coordinating the workshops and seeing the agenda through to production with the Institute of Electrical and Electronics Engineers (IEEE). We also thank Torsten Möller, who acted as the publishing liaison with IEEE. His expertise with the publication process at IEEE was invaluable to the team. We also want to thank the PNNL editorial and layout staff, Sharon Eaton and

Jamie Gority, for their persistence in getting this book to production, and Kristin Manke and Barbara Wilson for generously sharing their wisdom and experience. We also gratefully acknowledge Lee Ann Dudney and Christian Posse for their insight and suggestions. Finally, we recognize Ian Roberts and Ted Tanasse for enabling graphics and web designs for the online and print versions of *Illuminating the Path*.

The teamwork and spirit of collaboration displayed in producing this R&D agenda are exactly what is needed to make the agenda a reality. Thank you, team, for being a model for carrying this important work forward.

James J. Thomas   Kristin A. Cook

Table of Contents

Executive Summary

Motivation

Our country faces profound challenges that must be addressed to ensure our continued freedom and security. As the September 11, 2001, attacks on the Pentagon and World Trade Center illustrate, threats to the United States are present within our borders. On that day, after at least 20 months of planning and preparation, 19 terrorists hijacked four airliners at three different airports in a coordinated attack that resulted in the deaths of nearly 3000 people.

As the attack unfolded, government agencies and emergency response personnel had to respond in real time to an event of unprecedented scope. They were forced to assess situations and make decisions under extreme pressure, often without having critical information that would help them save additional lives [National Commission on Terrorist Attacks, 2004].

Focus on Homeland Security

The September 11, 2001, terrorist attacks helped illuminate the need to focus and coordinate the efforts to secure our country. The US Department of Homeland Security (DHS) was established in 2003 to secure the American homeland and protect the American people. It responds to the nation's security objectives of:

- Preventing terrorist attacks within the United States
- Reducing America's vulnerability to terrorism
- Minimizing the damage and recovering from attacks that do occur [Department of Homeland Security, 2004].

As stated in their Strategic Plan, the mission of DHS is to:

...lead the unified national effort to secure America. We will prevent and deter terrorist attacks and protect against and respond to threats and hazards to the Nation. We will ensure safe and secure borders, welcome lawful immigrants and visitors, and promote the free-flow of commerce.

DHS has identified strategic goals and objectives directed at accomplishing this mission (see box). Meeting these objectives requires the concerted efforts of professionals in fields as diverse as border and transportation security, intelligence analysis, law enforcement, and emergency preparedness and response (including firefighting and medical professions).

Grand Challenge: Enabling Profound Insights

One challenge underlies all of these objectives: the *analysis* of overwhelming amounts of disparate, conflicting, and dynamic information to identify and prevent emerging threats, protect our borders, and respond in the event of an attack or other disaster. This analysis process *requires human judgment* to make the best possible evaluation of incomplete, inconsistent, and potentially deceptive information in the face of rapidly changing situations.

Employing today's best practices in these areas and using the best possible training, technologies, and processes will still not position the country to meet the growing needs to protect our security. The scale of data is staggering, and our ability to collect data is increasing at a faster rate than our ability to analyze it. Although massive amounts of information are available from multiple sources, the relevant information content exists in a few nuggets. New methods are required that will allow the analyst to examine this massive, multi-dimensional, multi-source, time-varying information stream to make decisions in a time-critical manner.

Three major areas deserve particular focus: analyzing terrorist threats, safeguarding borders and ports, and preparing for and responding to emergencies. Threat analytics is the initial priority, given its importance in preventing attacks. These three areas are discussed in greater detail in Chapter 1.

Analyzing terrorist threats

An urgent goal is to stop terrorist attacks before they occur. Analysts need the ability to piece together information buried in disparate data—including immigration records; patterns of travel; telephone calls; and names, affiliations, and locations of suspected terrorists—to enable them to spot an emerging attack before it can be executed. Current technologies do not address the needs for handling these massive, messy, diverse, and ever-changing volumes of information. Furthermore, current tools provide very little in the way of support for the complex tasks of the analysis and discovery process. Very few current tools address the need to communicate analytical results and products to their audiences.

Research is needed to create software that supports the most complex and time-consuming portions of the analytical process, so that analysts can respond to increasingly more complex questions.

DHS Strategic Goals and Objectives That Motivate This Agenda [US Department of Homeland Security, 2004]

1) **Awareness**: Identify and understand threats, assess vulnerabilities, determine potential impacts and disseminate timely information to our homeland security partners and the American public.

   Gather and fuse all terrorism related intelligence; analyze, and coordinate access to information related to potential terrorist or other threats. (Objective 1.1)

   Identify and assess the vulnerability of critical infrastructure and key assets. (Objective 1.2)

   Develop timely, actionable, and valuable information based on intelligence analysis and vulnerability assessments. (Objective 1.3)

   Ensure quick and accurate dissemination of relevant intelligence information to homeland security partners, including the public. (Objective 1.4)

2) **Prevention**: Detect, deter and mitigate threats to our homeland.

   Secure our borders against terrorists, means of terrorism, illegal drugs and other illegal activity. (Objective 2.1)

   Provide operational end users with the technology and capabilities to detect and prevent terrorist attacks, means of terrorism and other illegal activities. (Objective 2.3)

   Ensure that national and international policy, law enforcement and other actions to prepare for and prevent terrorism are coordinated. (Objective 2.4)

3) **Protection**: Safeguard our people and their freedoms, critical infrastructures, property and the economy of our nation from acts of terrorism, natural disasters, or other emergencies.

   Strengthen nationwide preparedness and mitigation against acts of terrorism, natural disasters, or other emergencies. (Objective 3.7)

4) **Response**: Lead, manage and coordinate the national response to acts of terrorism, natural disasters, or other emergencies.

   Reduce the loss of life and property by strengthening nationwide response readiness. (Objective 4.1)

5) **Recovery**: Lead national, state, local and private sector efforts to restore services and rebuild communities after acts of terrorism, natural disasters, or other emergencies.

   Strengthen nationwide plans and capabilities. (Objective 5.1)

6) **Service**: Serve the public effectively by facilitating lawful trade, travel and immigration.

   Facilitate the efficient movement of legitimate cargo and people. (Objective 6.4)

7) **Organizational Excellence**: Value our most important resource, our people. Create a culture that promotes a common identity, innovation, mutual respect, accountability, and teamwork to achieve efficiencies, effectiveness, and operational synergies.

   Protect confidentiality and data integrity to ensure privacy and security. (Objective 7.1)

Safeguarding borders and ports

Safeguarding our borders is a complex task. Border guards and customs agents must prevent the illegal entry of goods and people into the country, while ensuring the free flow of legal commerce.

Daily, thousands of decisions must be made at each point of entry to discriminate between normal, legal activity and potential illegal activity. Although tools exist to help border and customs agents make these decisions, we need rapid advancement in these tools to better support the decision-making process.

Preparing for and responding to emergencies

Even with the greatest of vigilance, attacks can still occur. Emergency preparedness and response is critical to ensuring that, in the event of an attack or any other national disaster, loss of life and property is minimized.

Even with the well-developed emergency plans and procedures that already exist, several areas remain in which understanding and sharing of information can enhance our ability to respond and reduce the impact of an attack. We need real-time analytical monitoring that can alert first responders to unusual situations in advance. We also need software that helps support the demands of all the varying types of communications needed for different audiences in an emergency situation.

Visual Analytics: Responding to the Challenge

Research and development (R&D) in visual analytics helps address these challenges.

Visual analytics is the science of analytical reasoning facilitated by interactive visual interfaces. People use visual analytics tools and techniques to synthesize information and derive insight from massive, dynamic, ambiguous, and often conflicting data; detect the expected and discover the unexpected; provide timely, defensible, and understandable assessments; and communicate assessment effectively for action.

Visual analytics is a multidisciplinary field that includes the following focus areas:

- *Analytical reasoning techniques* that enable users to obtain deep insights that directly support assessment, planning, and decision making
- *Visual representations and interaction techniques* that take advantage of the human eye's broad bandwidth pathway into the mind to allow users to see, explore, and understand large amounts of information at once
- *Data representations and transformations* that convert all types of conflicting and dynamic data in ways that support visualization and analysis
- Techniques to support *production, presentation, and dissemination* of the results of an analysis to communicate information in the appropriate context to a variety of audiences.

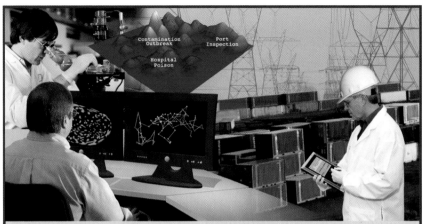

Visual analytics research and development facilitate threat identification, prevention, and response.

Defining the Research and Development Agenda for Visual Analytics

DHS chartered the National Visualization and Analytics Center™ (NVAC™) in 2004 with the goal of helping to counter future terrorist attacks in the US and around the globe. NVAC is a national resource that provides strategic direction and coordination of activities to discover, develop, and implement innovative visual information analysis methods. A major objective for NVAC is to define a 5-year R&D agenda for visual analytics to address the most pressing needs for R&D to facilitate advanced analytical insight. In spring 2004, NVAC formed a panel of distinguished researchers from academia, industry, and the national laboratory system, as well as select government experts. Through a series of workshops and collaborative efforts, the team established the plan for action summarized in this book.

This agenda builds upon and extends recent government publications, most notably two reports by the National Academy of Sciences. *Making the Nation Safer* [Alberts & Wulf, 2002] describes how science and technology can be used to protect the nation against terrorism. *Information Technology for Counterterrorism* [Hennessy et al., 2003] expands upon the work of *Making the Nation Safer*, focusing specifically on the opportunities for information technology to help counter and respond to terrorist attacks.

Although the agenda described herein is focused specifically on meeting homeland security challenges, the new capabilities created will have an impact on a wide variety of fields ranging from business to scientific research, in which understanding complex and dynamic information is important.

This agenda presents recommendations to advance the state of the art in the major visual analytics research areas:

- The science of analytical reasoning
- Visual representations and interaction techniques
- Data representations and transformations
- Production, presentation, and dissemination.

However, advancing the state of the technology is not sufficient to protect our homeland. We must accelerate the ability to move the most promising research into practice, and we must set the stage for an enduring visual analytics research community through a combination of education and research collaboration. This research agenda includes recommendations to meet these needs as well.

The Science of Analytical Reasoning (Chapter 2)

The science of analytical reasoning provides the reasoning framework upon which one can build both strategic and tactical visual analytics technologies for threat analysis, prevention, and response. This reasoning process is central to the analyst's task of applying human judgments to reach conclusions from a combination of evidence and assumptions. Analysis may require collaborative effort, especially in emergency response and border security contexts.

The goal of visual analytics is to facilitate this analytical reasoning process through the creation of software that maximizes human capacity to perceive, understand, and reason about complex and dynamic data and situations. It must build upon an understanding of the reasoning process, as well as an understanding of underlying cognitive and perceptual principles, to provide mission-appropriate interactions that allow analysts to have a true discourse with their information. The goal is to facilitate high-quality human judgment with a limited investment of the analysts' time.

Several actions are necessary to advance the science of analytical reasoning in support of visual analytics.

Recommendation

Build upon theoretical foundations of reasoning, sense-making, cognition, and perception to create visually enabled tools to support collaborative analytic reasoning about complex and dynamic problems.

To truly support the analytical reasoning process, we must enable the analyst to focus on what is truly important. We must support the processes involved in making sense of information and developing and evaluating alternative explanations. Tools and techniques must support both *convergent thinking*, which involves assembling evidence to find an answer, and *divergent thinking*, which involves thinking creatively to ensure that plausible alternatives have not been overlooked. These tools and techniques also must allow analysts to look at their problem at multiple levels of abstraction and support reasoning about situations that change over time, sometimes very rapidly. They must support collaboration and team-work, often among people with very different backgrounds and levels of expertise. Accomplishing this will require the development of theory to describe how interactive visual discourse works, both perceptually and cognitively, in support of analytical reasoning.

Recommendation

Conduct research to address the challenges and seize the opportunities posed by the scale of the analytic problem. The issues of scale are manifested in many ways, including the complexity and urgency of the analytical task, the massive volume of diverse and dynamic data involved in the analysis, and challenges of collaborating among groups of people involved in analysis, prevention, and response efforts.

The sheer volume and scale of data involved in the analytical process offer as many opportunities as they do challenges for visual analytics. A science of scalable, visually based analytical reasoning, or visual analytic discourse, must take the issue of scale into consideration. Different types of analytic discourse will be appropriate to different analytical tasks, based on the level of complexity of the task, the speed with which a conclusion must be reached, the data volumes and types, and the level of collaboration involved.

Visual Representations and Interaction Technologies (Chapter 3)

Visual representations and interaction technologies provide the mechanism for allowing the user to see and understand large volumes of information at once. The human mind can understand complex information received through visual channels. Visual analytics builds upon this ability to facilitate the analytical reasoning process.

Scientific principles for depicting information must provide the basis for visual representations, and principles are needed for new interaction approaches to support analytical techniques. Together, these foundations provide the basis for new visual paradigms that can scale to support analytical reasoning in many situations.

Visual design theory is more mature than interaction theory, so investments in the further development of interaction theory should take priority. Interaction theory must take into account the time constraints associated with varying levels of urgency in an analytic task. The application of visual representations and interactions must necessarily be adapted to fit the needs of the task at hand. The issues of scale also profoundly affect the design of visual representations and interactions and must be considered explicitly in the design of new visual representation and interaction techniques.

Creating effective visual representations is a labor-intensive process that requires a solid understanding of the visualization pipeline, characteristics of the data to be displayed, and the tasks to be performed. Currently, most visualization software is written with incomplete knowledge of at least some of this information. Generally, it is not possible for the analyst, who has the best understanding of the data and task, to construct new tools. We need new methods for constructing visually based systems that simplify the development process and result in better-targeted applications.

The panel makes several high-level recommendations aimed at addressing these challenges.

Recommendation

Create a science of visual representations based on cognitive and perceptual principles that can be deployed through engineered, reusable components. Visual representation principles must address all types of data, address scale and information complexity, enable knowledge discovery through information synthesis, and facilitate analytical reasoning.

Visual representations and interaction techniques provide the analyst and the first responder with their understanding of developing situations so that they may take action. A science of visual representations has been developed to support scientific applications, but different visual representations are needed to address the diverse data types that are relevant to homeland security missions. These data must be combined and presented to the user in a way that allows the user to understand their meaning, regardless of the data type or format of the original data. The goal is to expose all relevant data in a way that facilitates the reasoning process to enable action.

Recommendation

Develop a new suite of visual paradigms that support the analytical reasoning process.

These visualizations must:

- Facilitate understanding of massive and continually growing collections of data of multiple types
- Provide frameworks for analysis of spatial and temporal data
- Support understanding of uncertain, incomplete, and often misleading information
- Provide user- and task-adaptable, guided representations that enable full situation awareness while supporting development of detailed actions
- Support multiple levels of data and information abstraction
- Facilitate knowledge discovery through information synthesis, which is the integration of data based on their meaning rather than the original data type.

No one visual paradigm can address all possible tasks and situations. Therefore, we recommend developing a suite of visual paradigms that address multiple situations ranging from vulnerability analysis to real-time monitoring to emergency response support. The scale of data, especially in the forms of sensor, text, and imagery, is rapidly growing. Data are continually growing and changing, and visual representations must help analysts understand the changing nature of their data and the situations they represent. Likewise, many data are associated with a particular place and time. Representing these spatial and temporal qualities is necessary to provide analytical understanding. Furthermore, the visualization process is complicated by the need to support understanding of missing, conflicting, and deceptive information in an analytic discourse that is guided by the individual's knowledge and his or her task.

Recommendation

Develop a new science of interactions that supports the analytical reasoning process. This interaction science must provide a taxonomy of interaction techniques ranging from the low-level interactions to more complex interaction techniques and must address the challenge to scale across different types of display environments and tasks.

Interaction is the fuel for analytic discourse. Although the fundamental principles of interaction have been around for more than a decade, they do not address the needs for higher-order interaction techniques, such as task-directed or hypothesis-guided discourse, to support the analysis process. A new scientific theory and practice are critical to address the complexity of homeland security needs for analysis, prevention, and response. These interaction techniques must adapt to the particular dimensions of the analytical situation, ranging from longer-term analytical assessments to urgent and highly stressful emergency response support tasks. These interactions must be adaptable for use in platforms ranging from the large displays in emergency management control rooms to field-deployable handheld devices in the hands of first responders. This is a high priority for initial investments.

Data Representations and Transformations (Chapter 4)

Visualization is intended to represent data and information in a way that can be acted upon by the analyst. The quality of the visualization is most directly affected by the quality of the data representation that underlies the visualization.

Data must be transformed into a representation that is appropriate to the analytical task and appropriately conveys the important content of a large, complex, and dynamic collection. A data transformation is a computational procedure that converts between data representations. Data transformations are used to augment data by deriving additional data. Data transformations are used to convert data into new, semantically meaningful forms. For example, linguistic analysis can be used to assign meaning to the words in a text document. Data transformations may be used to determine the optimal way to display data, such as by creating a two-dimensional or three-dimensional representation of data with hundreds or thousands of dimensions.

Transforming and representing data are complex for many reasons. The first issue is the sheer number of different types of data that may be analyzed: text in the form of short or long documents comprising many languages, numeric data from sensors, structured data from relational databases, audio and video, and image data. Each of these types of data may need to be transformed in different ways to facilitate visual analysis.

The massive scale and dynamic nature of data dictate that the transformations must be fast, flexible, and capable of operating at many levels of abstraction. Data are of varying levels of certainty and reliability, so these assessments of quality must be preserved and presented. Data of different types are often required to conduct an analysis, so it is very important to develop a data synthesis capability—a capability to bring data of different types together in a single environment so that analysts can concentrate on the meaning of the data rather than on the form in which it was originally packaged.

The panel recommends several actions to advance the community's capabilities for data representation and transformation.

Recommendation

Develop both theory and practice for transforming data into new scalable representations that faithfully represent the content of the underlying data.

From the standpoint of the analyst, border guard, or first responder, information provides guidance, insight, and support for assessments and decisions. Our goal is to illuminate the potentially interesting content within the data so that users may discover important and unexpected information buried within massive volumes of data. Each type of data presents its own challenges for data representation and transformation. In most cases, data representations are not meant to replace the original data but to augment them by highlighting relevant nuggets of information to facilitate analysis.

We must develop mathematical transformations and representations that can scale to deal with vast amounts of data in a timely manner. These approaches must provide a high-fidelity representation of the true information content of the underlying data. They must support the need to analyze a problem at varying levels of abstraction and consider the same data from multiple viewpoints.

Data are dynamic and may be found in ever-growing collections or in streams that may never be stored. New representation methods are needed to accommodate the dynamic and sometimes transient nature of data. Transformation methods must include techniques to detect changes, anomalies, and emerging trends.

Methods exist at varying levels of maturity for transforming data. For example, there are a variety of methods for transforming the content of textual documents using either statistical or semantic approaches. Combining the strengths of these two approaches may greatly improve the results of the transformation.

Recommendation

Create methods to synthesize information of different types and from different sources into a unified data representation so that analysts, first responders, and border personnel may focus on the meaning of the data.

Complex analytical tasks require the user to bring together evidence from a variety of data types and sources, including text sources in multiple languages, audio, video, and sensor data. Today's analytical tools generally require that the user consider data of different types separately. However, users need to be able to understand the meaning of their information and to consider all the evidence together, without being restricted by the type of data that the evidence originally came in. Furthermore, they need to be able to consider their information at different levels of abstraction.

Synthesis is essential to the analysis process. While it is related to the concept of data fusion, it entails much more than placing information of different types on a map display. The analytical insight required to meet homeland security missions requires the integration of relationships, transactions, images, and video at the true meaning level. While spatial elements may be displayed on a map, the non-spatial information must be synthesized at the meaning level with that spatial information and presented to the user in a unified representation.

Recommendation

Develop methods and principles for representing data quality, reliability, and certainty measures throughout the data transformation and analysis process.

By nature, data are of varying quality, and most data have levels of uncertainty associated with them. Furthermore, the reliability of data may differ based on a number of factors, including the data source. As data are combined and transformed, the uncertainties may become magnified. These uncertainties may have profound effects on the analytical process and must be portrayed to users to inform their thinking. They will also make their own judgments of data quality, uncertainty, and reliability, based upon their expertise. These judgments must be captured and incorporated as well. Furthermore, in this environment of constant change, assessments of data quality or uncertainty may be called into question at any time based on the existence of new and conflicting information.

The complexity of this problem will require algorithmic advances to address the establishment and maintenance of uncertainty measures at varying levels of data abstraction.

Production, Presentation, and Dissemination (Chapter 5)

Production, presentation, and dissemination of results are often the most time-consuming part of analysis. It is the phase that technologists think of last but is the only part of the process that is visible to the consumers of analysis. In emergency situations or in day-to-day analysis, technology could make the largest improvement in this part of the analysis process. Our goal is to bring our R&D efforts to bear so that we can greatly reduce the time it takes for analysis results to be shared with their audiences, while dramatically improving the effectiveness of this communication.

Production is the creation of materials that summarize the results of an analytical effort. Presentation is the packaging of those materials in a way that helps the audience understand the analytical results in context and using terms that are meaningful to them. Dissemination is the process of sharing that information with the intended audience.

The production and presentation of reports requires the incorporation of design and rhetoric. Multiple homeland security audiences and the immediacy of their needs for analytic results will spur the cooperation of visualization and graphic production developers as well as the development of rhetorical design capabilities within the workflow. The future holds the promise of immediate communication of well-analyzed results in emerging and emergency situations in the homeland.

The panel recommends several actions to advance the capabilities for production, presentation, and dissemination.

Recommendation

Develop methodology and tools that enable the capture of the analytic assessment, decision recommendations, and first responder actions into information packages. These packages must be tailored for each intended receiver and situation and permit expansion to show supporting evidence as needed.

No matter what the end information product, the need to describe it, link it to its sources, describe its level of certainty, and put it into the context of the intended user is a time-consuming task. Few scientific methods or tool suites support creation of the end product. This is a high-priority area for near-term investments.

Recommendation

Develop technologies that enable analysts to communicate what they know through the use of appropriate visual metaphor and accepted principles of reasoning and graphic representation. Create techniques that enable effective use of limited, mobile forms of technologies to support situation assessment by first responders. Support the need for effective public alerts with the production of a basic handbook for common methods for communicating risks.

Emergency situations and the need for rapid, accurate communication for informed action by management, first responders, and the public bring to the forefront the need for analysts to effectively communicate what they know. Communications must facilitate teamwork that may include the public as current AMBER Alerts do. To motivate proper actions, the reasoning behind the results must be made as visible as the results themselves to decision makers.

Recommendation

Create visual analytics data structures, intermediate representations, and outputs that support seamless integration of tools so that data requests and acquisition, visual analysis, note-taking, presentation composition, and dissemination all take place within a cohesive environment that supports around-the-clock operation and provides robust privacy and security control.

The task of production can be accelerated and greatly enhanced in quality by a new science, methods, and tools to capture intermediate presentations of analysis, support mid-level assessments, and support note-taking, directly within the analytical reasoning processes. The framework for this must take into account security and privacy policies.

Moving Research into Practice (Chapter 6)

To truly leverage the successful research results described by this agenda, these results must be moved into practice. They must be deployed and used to address the national security and analysis needs of the country.

The issues associated with moving research into practice are often omitted from R&D agendas of this type. However, this panel felt compelled to provide a framework for four fundamental issues associated with accelerating the process of getting technology into the hands of users. Each of these issues has the potential to make or break the successful deployment of the new technologies we are recommending.

First and foremost, the resulting tools, algorithms, and approaches must be evaluated to ensure that they represent a significant advance over current practice and to ensure that they operate correctly. Second, issues of security and privacy must be addressed from the start and throughout the research, development, and deployment process. Third, software interoperability, architecture, and data handling must be attended to in order to facilitate collaborative research, software evaluation, and software deployment into a wide variety of software environments. Finally, a concerted and sustained effort to insert the resulting technology into operational environments will be essential if the research results are to be of benefit.

The panel recommends several actions to accelerate the transitioning of research into practice.

Recommendation

Develop an infrastructure to facilitate evaluation of new visual analytics technologies.

All too often we develop and deploy technology that has not been evaluated within the contexts of its intended use. This is especially true when dealing with the bridge between unclassified and classified applications. We need common methods and measures for evaluation, with a focus not only on performance but also on utility.

Evaluation is an iterative process that will require a support infrastructure in order to succeed. It begins with evaluations of research done by the inventors themselves. Good sources of unclassified test data will be required to support this evaluation. The most promising research will mature through further stages of development and refinement and will be combined with other technologies, with progressively more sophisticated evaluations conducted in unclassified visual analytics test beds that will be established to approximate the target deployment environment. Conducting these evaluations will require a test bed infrastructure with more representative, but still unclassified, test data streams to use for evaluation. Ultimately, tools will be evaluated in technology insertion facilities that directly replicate the target production environments, which will require close collaboration among government and research communities. The lessons learned throughout the evaluation process should be captured from this process and shared throughout the community.

Recommendation

Create and use a common security and privacy infrastructure, with support for incorporating privacy-supporting technologies, such as data minimization and data anonymization.

Protecting confidentiality and data integrity to ensure privacy and security is a key objective of DHS. As stated in their Strategic Plan [DHS, 2004], "We will ensure the technologies employed sustain, and do not erode, privacy protections relating to the collection, use, and disclosure of personal information. We will eliminate inappropriate access to confidential data to preserve the privacy of Americans. We will maintain an appropriate balance between freedom and safety consistent with the values of our society."

The goal of visual analytics R&D is to create fundamentally new ways for people to understand and act upon the data available to them. However, this must be done within a framework that fully considers and supports the need for privacy in all phases of the work, from the earliest research stages to the deployment phase.

To make attention to privacy a natural and routine part of the visual analytics R&D process, we need to adopt a standard suite of anonymization technologies and make these available to the visual analytics research community. We further recommend that all researchers in visual analytics receive training so that they clearly understand privacy and security laws and policies and do not inadvertently invent technologies or use data that violate these laws and policies.

Recommendation

Use a common component-based software development approach for visual analytics software to facilitate evaluation of research results in integrated prototypes and deployment of promising components in diverse operational environments.

Software interoperability is important to the visual analytics R&D effort. Initially, complementary technologies created by different research teams will be evaluated together in test beds to determine how best to deploy them. Ultimately, though, the most promising breakthrough technologies are likely to have broad applicability and thus will be candidates for deployment into diverse analyst-focused systems in use within DHS and other government agencies. The only effective path to rapid and cost-effective deployment of new technologies is to develop them in the form of reusable software components.

Recommendation

Identify and publicize best practices for inserting visual analytics technologies into operational environments.

One measure of success for this R&D agenda is the extent to which the resulting research matures into software that finds broad usage. The process of transitioning software into wide analytical use is complex, and it requires the cooperative efforts of researchers, software engineers, systems infrastructure and operations staff, training and support staff, and the users themselves. Although the process can be difficult, there are examples of successful transitions that provide important lessons and guideposts for future technology insertion efforts. By identifying and publicizing these best practices, we can help speed the transition of the next generation of innovative research into the user's hands.

Positioning for Enduring Success (Chapter 7)

Achieving the agenda outlined here will require the sustained efforts of a multidisciplinary community of researchers. Educational efforts and partnerships are necessary to establish and sustain an enduring visual analytics R&D community capable of meeting these challenges.

Recommendation

Develop programs to support education of the research community about the drivers for visual analytics research.

Two major educational efforts are required. First, we must work in conjunction with universities to influence university curricula to provide formal education about visual analytics needs and challenges. Second, we must provide an active continuing education program through workshops, tutorials, and conferences to provide a broad understanding of analytic needs, technical challenges, and state-of-the-art R&D results. These forums should bring together practitioners from government, academia, industry, and the national laboratory system.

Recommendation

Form university-led centers of excellence as well as partnerships with government, industry, national laboratories, and selected international research entities to bring together the best talents to accomplish the visual analytics R&D agenda.

NVAC should be the coordinating point for the achievement of the visual analytics research agenda. University-led centers of excellence should be established to focus on advancement of specific high-priority portions of the agenda. Partnerships with government agencies must also be established to help accomplish this agenda.

In addition, opportunities must be provided so that experts outside academia can contribute to advancement of this agenda. Avenues must be provided for partnerships with researchers, both individually and organizationally, in industry, government, and the national laboratory system. Selected international collaborations and partnerships should also be established to accomplish portions of the research mission.

Recommendation

Establish special partnerships with the Corporate Information Office (CIO) organizations that support mission agencies to facilitate technology insertion within their operational environments.

Transitioning technology into operation is a complex challenge and requires intimate knowledge of the domain into which the technology will be deployed. Partnerships with user organizations and their supporting CIO offices can supply the necessary insight to understand the analytical needs and the operational constraints for software being deployed. These insights are key to accelerating the process of transitioning research into operation.

Recommendation

Provide ongoing support for collaborations, internships, staff exchanges, educational material development, and other efforts that help build interest in the missions of homeland security.

This is a critical need to meet DHS's mission of enduring security for the homeland. This educational outreach effort should be coordinated with the DHS Educational Programs Office and stimulated by coordinated learning and training investments.

Call to Action

The agenda described herein is only a beginning. As the new discipline of visual analytics matures during the next few years, our understanding of the research challenges and priorities will grow rapidly.

To remain on target for accomplishing this research agenda, we will periodically evaluate its progress. While success may be measured in many ways, we choose to focus on two specific areas for evaluation. This effort will be a success if:

- New visual analytic techniques are being transitioned into practice
- A vibrant and growing community of practice has been established for visual analytics researchers and engineers.

This R&D agenda constitutes a grand challenge. While DHS is providing the foundational support for this effort, its success must be realized through the coordinated support and efforts of multiple government agencies, industry, academia, and the national laboratories. As we mobilize to address this challenge, we are mindful of the role we play in helping to safeguard our nation.

References

Alberts B and WA Wulf. 2002. *Making the Nation Safer: The Role of Science and Technology in Countering Terrorism*. National Academy of Sciences, Washington, D.C.

Department of Homeland Security (DHS). 2004. *Securing our Homeland: U.S. Department of Homeland Security Strategic Plan*. Available at http://www.dhs.gov/interweb/assetlibrary/DHS_ StratPlan_FINAL_spread.pdf.

Hennessy JL, DA Patterson, and HS Lin, eds. 2003. *Information Technology for Counterterrorism: Immediate Actions and Future Possibilities*. National Academy of Sciences, Washington, D.C.

National Commission on Terrorist Attacks. 2004. *The 9/11 Commission Report*. W.W. Norton and Company, Ltd., New York.

"The purpose of computing is insight, not numbers."
—Richard Hamming (1915–1998)

Grand Challenges

Our country faces profound challenges that must be addressed in order to ensure our continued freedom and security. As the September 11, 2001, attacks on the Pentagon and World Trade Center illustrate, threats to the United States are present within our borders. On that day, after at least 20 months of planning and preparation, 19 terrorists hijacked four airliners at three different airports in a coordinated attack. The hijackers crashed two planes into the World Trade Center's twin towers and one plane into the Pentagon. The fourth plane, intended to attack another US landmark, crashed in a field in Pennsylvania. These attacks claimed the lives of 2973 people.

As the attack unfolded, government agencies and emergency response personnel "...struggled, under difficult circumstances, to improvise a homeland defense against an unprecedented challenge they had never before encountered and had never trained to meet." They were forced to assess complex and dynamic situations and make decisions rapidly under extreme pressure, often without access to critical information that would help them save additional lives [National Commission on Terrorist Attacks, 2004].

Protecting Our Homeland

Providing for the security of the US and its citizens constitutes a grand challenge for our country. Future attacks could result in major loss of life and shake the nation's confidence in its fundamental security. The US Department of Homeland Security (DHS) was established in 2003 to secure the American homeland and protect the American people. It responds to the nation's security objectives of preventing terrorist attacks within the US, reducing America's vulnerability to terrorism, and minimizing the damage and recovering from attacks that do occur [Department of Homeland Security, 2004].

As described in their Strategic Plan, the mission of DHS is to:

... Lead the unified national effort to secure America. We will prevent and deter terrorist attacks and protect against and respond to threats and hazards to the nation. We will ensure safe and secure borders, welcome lawful immigrants and visitors, and promote the free-flow of commerce.

DHS has identified strategic goals and objectives to accomplish this important mission. Meeting these objectives requires the concerted efforts of professionals in fields as diverse as border and transportation security, intelligence analysis, law enforcement, and emergency preparedness and response (including the firefighting and medical professions). These people are challenged daily with making sense of vast amounts of conflicting and ever-changing information to identify and prevent emerging threats, protect our borders, and respond in the event of an attack or other disaster.

To understand the complexity of this challenge, consider two imagined scenarios.

Scenario 1: Sarin Gas Attack

An organized international terrorist group develops a plot to conduct a Sarin gas attack in the US.

According to the Centers for Disease Control, "Sarin is a human-made chemical warfare agent classified as a nerve agent. Nerve agents are the most toxic and rapidly acting of the known chemical warfare agents." Pure Sarin gas is odorless, so people may not be aware that they have been exposed. Sarin gas attacks the respiratory system and can be fatal [http://www.bt.cdc.gov/agent/sarin/basics/facts.asp].

The terrorist organization sends a planning team to the US to identify the target for this attack. After examining several options, they select three large commercial office buildings in a major metropolitan area. They develop a plan to release the Sarin gas into the ventilation systems of the building. The target buildings are chosen based on their size and location, as well as the relative ease of access to their ventilation systems. The terrorists set up a cell in the target city, and three obtain jobs in building maintenance for the office buildings.

In the meantime, an overseas terrorist cell acquires the Sarin nerve agent, packs it carefully to conceal its true contents, and ships it into the US via a sea-borne cargo container. It passes through Customs at a port city and makes its way to the US-based terrorist cell via rental truck to a safe house near the target city. The overseas cell also acquires protective safety gear and ships it to the US-based terrorist cell.

The local terrorist cell builds the necessary spray dispersal devices, acquiring materials from local stores as needed. On the day of the attack, the terrorists working at the target buildings put on protective equipment and deploy their dispersal devices in the ventilation system, following a strict time schedule to conduct a coordinated attack. Then, as the attackers flee the area, the Sarin gas permeates the air in the three office buildings and escapes though rooftop ventilation systems to the outside air as well.

Within a couple of minutes, people in the three buildings begin to experience the symptoms of exposure. Calls to 911 are placed, and emergency personnel rush to the scene. Initial emergency crews on the scene are unlikely to realize that there has been a terrorist attack and that a nerve agent has been released throughout the buildings, leading them to rush into the building without any protective equipment and suffer exposure themselves.

It may take many minutes, and significant loss of life, before emergency response crews observe enough clues to piece together the true nature of the emergency and identify the agent as Sarin gas. Then they must quickly determine how best to rescue and treat survivors. In addition, because Sarin has been released into the air outside the buildings, emergency managers and city officials must communicate with the public to make clear to them to shelter in place to avoid exposure. Those officials and managers will need to also clearly state the potential for exposure and harm to avoid panic among the public.

Scenario 2: Biological Attack

An international terrorist organization conducts an operation to produce an outbreak of pneumonic plague. Plague is caused by a bacterium, and death will ensue if the infection is not treated rapidly with antibiotics. It can readily spread among humans.

The terrorist organization identifies a major metropolitan area to target for the release of the plague. They select three high-traffic areas as targets: in the bathrooms of the city's major airport, in the bathrooms of its professional sports arena, and in the city's train station.

The plague bacteria are transported into the country via truck at a major border crossing and are driven to the target city. Over the course of one day, local members of the terrorist organization release the plague canisters in the three target locations, timing each release to coincide with the heaviest traffic at each of the locations. The release goes undetected.

Travelers infected in the airport fly to their destinations, both across the US and to other countries. Likewise, tourists in town for the sporting event return to their homes in other locations.

No sign of illness appears until about 36 hours after the initial attack, when infected people rapidly experience severe respiratory illness and die if not properly treated. The rapid increase in unexplained illnesses in the target city triggers alarms within the city's public health system, and public health officials become aware for the first time that an abnormal pattern is emerging. Investigation is required to determine that an abnormal event has occurred. Additional investigation allows the experts to identify that the illness is plague and eventually to tie the cases back to common sources. Multiple government agencies participate in investigations to identify the illness and address the public health needs, as well as to identify the plot behind the outbreak and apprehend those responsible.

While this investigation proceeds, the public in this city are growing worried, and they must be given instructions on the basis of preliminary information to help protect them from illness. By the time the cause is identified, infected individuals who have traveled across the country, and to other countries, are also falling ill and dying, but the reason for the illness will not initially be clear.

Because plague spreads easily among humans, the disease will have the potential to spread far beyond the originally infected population before it is finally identified. Plague has symptoms in common with many milder respiratory illnesses. Part of the major emergency response challenge will be to discriminate the true plague cases from worried members of the public with these milder illnesses. In addition, providing clear and specific information to the public about how to protect themselves from infection will be a high priority.

Grand Challenge: Enabling Profound Insights

The *analysis* of overwhelming amounts of disparate, conflicting, and dynamic information is central to identifying and preventing emerging threats, protecting our borders, and responding in the event of an attack or other disaster. This analysis process *requires human judgment* to make the best possible evaluation of incomplete, inconsistent, and potentially deceptive information in the face of rapidly changing situations to both detect the expected and discover the unexpected. People must collaborate across organizations, agencies, and jurisdictions in a way that allows them to share information when appropriate while adhering to privacy laws and policies.

Employing today's best practices in these areas and using the best possible training, technologies, and processes will still not position the country to address the growing challenges to our security. The volume of data is staggering. Although massive amounts of information are available from multiple sources, the relevant information content exists in a few nuggets. New methods are required that will allow the analyst to examine this massive, multi-dimensional, multi-source, time-varying information stream to make decisions in a time-critical manner. By providing the experts with the capability to truly understand this information, we enable them to make better decisions that prevent and prepare for attacks, improve emergency response, and save lives.

Three major areas deserve particular focus: analyzing terrorist threats, safeguarding borders and ports, and preparing for and responding to emergencies. Strong analytic capabilities are required to accomplish all three of these tasks. Threat analytics is the initial priority, given its importance in the prevention of attacks.

Analyzing Terrorist Threats

As these scenarios illustrate, terrorists take great care to plan and orchestrate their attacks. An urgent goal is to stop terrorist attacks before they occur, which requires that analysts uncover the subtle clues that can identify specifics about the attack before it occurs. To prevent an attack, analysts must piece together details about who is going to conduct the attack, what the attackers plan to do, and where and when the attack will occur.

Observations, such as reports of strangers scouting out the ventilation systems of large buildings, play a critical role in helping to tip off authorities that something is amiss. Analysts need the ability to combine information buried in disparate data, including immigration records; patterns of travel; telephone calls; and names, affiliations, and locations of suspected terrorists, to allow them to piece together the information necessary to spot an emerging attack before it can be executed. In addition, information relating to potential threat agents, the materials and facilities used to make them, and their possible deployment must be considered.

Analysts evaluate potential vulnerabilities that exist in our country and identify and monitor potential threats that may arise. They are also alert for potential anomalies that may indicate that something unexpected is occurring.

Today, analysts have a select number of software programs available to help them organize their information, gain an overview of it, explore it, and examine high-level trends. Although these tools help the analyst, they are only scratching the surface in terms of meeting true analytical needs. Current technologies cannot address the needs for handling the massive, messy, and ever-changing volumes of information and the diversity of types of information. Furthermore, current analytical tools provide basic capabilities, such as query and search, but provide very little in the way of support for the complex tasks of the analysis, synthesis, and discovery process. Very few current tools address the need to communicate analytical results and products to their audiences.

Research is needed to create software that supports the most complex and time-consuming portions of the analytical process, so that analysts can respond to increasingly more complex questions.

Safeguarding Borders and Ports

Safeguarding borders is a complex task. Border guards and customs agents must prevent the illegal entry of goods or people into the country, while allowing them to ensure the free flow of legal commerce.

Daily, thousands of decisions must be made at each point of entry to discriminate between normal, legal activity and potential illegal activity. Tools and processes have been developed to help border and customs agents make these decisions. However, because of the volume of potentially relevant information and the speed with which decisions must be made, we need rapid advancement in the software systems used to support this decision-making process. Individuals in the field need reach-back support to allow them to get more in-depth scientific assessment when necessary so that they can better discriminate illegal from legitimate cargo. At a national level, it is also important to be able to combine information about incidents at ports and borders with other available information to allow analysts to identify patterns that could indicate emerging terrorist threats.

Preparing for and Responding to Emergencies

Even with the greatest of vigilance, attacks can still occur. Emergency preparedness and response are critical to ensuring that, in the event of an attack or any other national disaster, loss of life and property is minimized.

Thorough preparation and response plans have been put in place for a large number of potential national emergencies, and emergency response training and practice drills are regularly held to hone our nation's capabilities. However, terrorist attacks often capitalize on the element of surprise to maximize their effectiveness. As the above scenarios illustrate, in some cases it is not apparent what kind of attack has taken place, or even (in the initial stages) that an attack has occurred at all. This kind of confusion delays the experts' ability to respond effectively. Coordinated attacks may be timed so that a secondary attack occurs once emergency response personnel have arrived, in order to further increase the impact of the attack.

Even with the well-developed emergency plans and procedures that exist, the above scenarios illustrate several areas in which understanding and sharing of information can greatly enhance our ability to respond and greatly reduce the impact of an attack. In the first scenario, for example, real-time analytical monitoring that alerts first responders to the anomalous frequency and location of 911 calls can raise their awareness of the unusual situation in advance. Emergency command centers need analytical capabilities to help them get to the root of emergency situations, rapidly identify the appropriate response, and coordinate ever-shifting facts during a chaotic and pressure-filled time.

Communication is also critical in an emergency situation. First responders must coordinate and communicate clearly across multiple jurisdictions. Sharing of information must be done carefully to protect both privacy and national security. As the scenarios show, communication with the general population is also a requirement. Meeting these communication requirements is time-consuming and challenging, because each audience requires a different type of communication to answer the questions that are most pertinent to them. New software is needed to help streamline the process of customizing communications for different audiences so that people can make better-informed decisions in emergencies.

The Scalability Challenge

Data are growing at an incredible rate. Lyman and Varian [2003] estimate that in 2002 alone, the world produced 5 exabytes (5×10^{18} bytes) of new stored information in the form of paper, film, and electronic media. Another 18 exabytes of streaming information was produced in 2002. Their study estimates that storage of new information is growing at a rate of more than 30% per year.

Analysts, emergency response teams, and border protection personnel have massive amounts of information available to them from multiple sources, but the important information may be hidden in a few nuggets. We must create new methods to allow the analyst to examine this massive, multi-dimensional, multi-source, time-varying information stream to make effective decisions in time-critical situations.

Data Characteristics

Consider some examples of data types that contribute to this information overload.

Textual data. Massive textual data can come from documents, speeches, news, e-mails, or web pages. These data are ever increasing in volume. Our target is to be able to support analysis of data volumes growing at a rate of one billion new structured messages or transactions per hour, and one million new unstructured messages or documents per hour.

Databases. Many corporate and government entities have constructed huge databases containing a wealth of information. These databases are both diverse and distributed. In addition, individuals and workgroups may have their own local databases that augment these large databases. New algorithms are required to permit efficient discovery of previously unknown patterns in these disparate databases.

Image data. Consider the data collected by satellites that image the earth. Commercial satellites can create images at 1-meter resolution and collectively create an image of the planet's land surface in a very short time. New methods are needed to permit efficient understanding of image data, especially in the context of other types of data mentioned here.

Sensor data. The revolution in miniaturization for computer systems has resulted in the production of many types of sensors. The sensors can collect data about their environment (location, proximity, temperature, light, radiation, etc.), can analyze these data, and can communicate among themselves. Collections of sensors can produce very large streaming sets of data. Methods are needed for analyzing sensor data to efficiently incorporate the data into computerized models to support border protection and emergency response.

Video data. Video is often used to enhance the effectiveness of high-risk security operations. Video recording and content analysis are being used in concert as a powerful tool for improving business processes and customer service. New techniques must be developed to integrate these capabilities for analyzing streaming video data into the analyst's toolkit.

The data present challenges not only because of their diversity, volume, and dynamic nature but also because the data are ambiguous, uncertain, and potentially intentionally deceptive. Data of multiple types must often be analyzed in concert to gain insight. Important data needed for correct interpretation may be missing, but this may or may not be apparent to the analyst. We must provide mechanisms that help the analyst visually understand the nature of the data being evaluated.

A grand challenge is to support the analyst in distilling the relevant nuggets of information from widely disparate information streams and create an information space containing relevant information that can be used by the analyst in reaching the most timely and well-informed assessment of the situation. We must provide mechanisms that can visualize the connections among relevant information in the information streams and allow the analyst to gain insight from data.

Scalability

Current technologies cannot support the scale and complexity of the growing analytical challenge. New techniques and underlying scientific foundations are needed to deal with the scale of the problems we are facing in threat analysis, emergency management, and border protection. Issues of scale cut across every aspect of this challenge.

When considering scalability issues, it is important to understand the context of the development of the computer industry as well as natural human skills and limitations. Moore's Law suggests that basic computer technology performance (processor speed and memory density) will double every 18 months. Recently, graphics technology has been improving performance at an even faster rate, doubling every 12 months. This trend has continued for 50 years, and some projections say it will continue for at least another 10 years before fundamental limitations of physics are encountered.

All of this added processing power and memory density has enabled the gathering and processing of vast amounts of data.

However, basic human skills and abilities do not change significantly over time. It is true that technology advances, applied carefully, can enable us to use a higher percentage of natural human abilities, but there are fundamental limits that we are asymptotically approaching. This situation gives rise to the popular notion of *information glut*. That is, we are able to access far more information than we, as humans, can possibly process. The situation also makes scalability issues more difficult to resolve. In addition, analytical challenges often require coping with, sharing, and using information at multiple scales simultaneously. Ultimately, large-scale problems have to be reduced to a scale that humans can comprehend and act on.

Scale brings opportunities as well. For example, increased scale may help reduce uncertainty of an emerging situation. In addition, large data volumes allow analysts to discover more complete information about a situation. As a result, analysts may be able to determine more easily when expected information is missing; sometimes the fact that information is missing offers important clues in the assessment of the situation.

Here, we consider five of the major scale issues that must be addressed: information scalability, visual scalability, display scalability, human scalability, and software scalability.

Information Scalability

Information scalability implies the capability to extract relevant information from massive data streams. Methods of information scalability include methods to filter and reduce the amount of data, techniques to represent the data in a multi-resolution manner, and methods to abstract the data sets.

A second form of information scalability has to do with the rate of change of the information. Most existing techniques do not handle dynamic change, but a few do.

Finally, information presentations must be scaled or adapted to the audience. For example, an analyst's presentation to other analysts will contain far more detail than the summary analysis presented to the President. Current techniques require that this be done manually in an ad hoc fashion.

Relevant information may appear at a variety of scales, and the user must be able to change between scales in a way that is easy to understand and track. We must be able to understand the cross-scale interactions. We must be able to handle a wide range of dynamic change, and we must develop systems that semi-automatically scale or adapt information presentations to match a target audience.

Visual Scalability

Visual scalability is the capability of visualization representation and visualization tools to effectively display massive data sets, in terms of either the number or the dimension of individual data elements [Eick & Karr, 2002]. Factors affecting visual scalability include the quality of visual displays, the visual metaphors used in the display of information, the techniques used to interact with the visual representations, and the perception capabilities of the human cognitive system.

Most published techniques in the field of information visualization handle data sets with hundreds to thousands of elements. Some techniques can scale to handle tens of thousands of elements, and a very few can handle hundreds of thousands up to one million elements. The InfoVis 2003 Contest focused on the problem of visualizing and comparing large hierarchies. The winning technique was TreeJuxtaposer [Munzner et al., 2003], which could handle two trees of about 100,000 elements and one tree up to 500,000 elements.

However, as described previously, some extreme situations may demand the processing of tens of millions of new documents per day, with a total database size of tens of billions of documents. It is reported that at least one existing database has 120 billion documents. It seems likely that these database sizes will increase over time. Clearly the current state of the art is far from able to visually represent today's data collections, and the need will continue to grow. New techniques are needed to bridge this gap.

Display Scalability

Most published visualization techniques are designed for one size display, generally a desktop display (typically 1280x1024 pixels). We need to develop techniques that scale to a variety of display form factors to take advantage of whatever capabilities are available to support analysis and collaboration. Tools should be able to make effective use of everything from a wall-sized display in an emergency response situation room to a PDA or phone-sized display in the hands of a first responder in the field. One major challenge is to develop interaction techniques that are display scale-independent. That is, consistent visualization and interaction techniques should be used regardless of display size. Studies need to be done to determine how to display information effectively, particularly on small displays.

Human Scalability

While human skills and abilities do not scale (i.e., they are relatively fixed), the number of humans involved in analytical problem-solving, border protection, and emergency preparedness and response activities does scale. Most published techniques for supporting analysis are targeted for a single user at a time. We must develop techniques that gracefully scale from a single user to a collaborative (multi-user) environment. Much of the relevant collaboration research is focused on small groups of collaborators (two or three people). In the scenarios we envision, users may be collaborating from within the same team in an organization, at different levels of an organization, or even in different organizations. Each of these cases has its own set of problems that must be solved. One scenario might involve a number of first responders, several regional emergency management centers, and a national emergency management center—that is, dozens of users collaborating through the use of shared analytical tools and focusing on different levels of information accessible by everyone involved.

Software Scalability

Software scalability is the capability of a software system to interactively manipulate large data sets. Software scalability includes the generation of new algorithms that scale to the ever-increasing information sets that we generate today. We wish to avoid the hidden costs that arise when we build and maintain monolithic, non-interacting, non-scalable software.

Other Scalability Issues

Cutting across many scalability issues are concerns with privacy and security, particularly when scaling to multi-user environments. Data privacy and security laws and policies must be adhered to rigorously, which means that software must address challenges such as protecting information from inappropriate access, down to the data item and individual user level. Privacy and security are discussed in more detail in Chapter 6.

Scalability issues also arise in dealing with geographically dispersed teams speaking different languages or using different terminology within the same language, and working across teams of people with differing expertise.

The Need for Visual Analytics

To meet the analytical needs described in this chapter, the scientific community must dramatically accelerate research and development (R&D) efforts to develop fundamentally new solutions. These solutions must enable analysts to focus their full cognitive and perceptual capabilities on their analytical processes, while allowing them to apply advanced computational capabilities to augment their discovery process. R&D in the field of visual analytics helps address these challenges.

Visual analytics is the science of analytical reasoning facilitated by interactive visual interfaces. People use visual analytics tools and techniques to synthesize information and derive insight from massive, dynamic, ambiguous, and often conflicting data; detect the expected and discover the unexpected; provide timely, defensible, and understandable assessments; and communicate assessment effectively for action.

Visual analytics integrates new computational and theory-based tools with innovative interactive techniques and visual representations to enable human-information discourse. The design of the tools and techniques is based on cognitive, design, and perceptual principles.

The Research and Development Agenda for Visual Analytics

DHS chartered the National Visualization and Analytics Center™ (NVAC™) in 2004 with the goal of helping to counter future terrorist attacks in the US and around the globe. NVAC is a national resource that provides strategic direction and coordination of activities to discover, develop, and implement innovative visual information analysis methods. A major objective for NVAC is to define a 5-year R&D agenda for visual analytics to address the most pressing needs for R&D to facilitate advanced analytical insight. In spring 2004, NVAC formed a panel of distinguished researchers from academia, industry, and the national laboratory system, as well as select government experts. Through a series of workshops and collaborative efforts, the team established the plan for action summarized in this book.

This agenda builds upon and extends recent government publications, most notably two reports by the National Academy of Sciences. *Making the Nation Safer* [Alberts & Wulf, 2002] describes how science and technology can be used to protect the nation against terrorism. *Information Technology for Counterterrorism* [Hennessy et al., 2003] expands upon the work of *Making the Nation Safer*, focusing specifically on the opportunities for information technology to help counter and respond to terrorist attacks.

Although the agenda described herein is focused specifically on meeting homeland security challenges, the new capabilities created will have an impact on a wide variety of fields ranging from business to scientific research, in which understanding complex and dynamic information is important.

The R&D agenda for visual analytics will require the assembly of a multidisciplinary team to address a set of interrelated research areas illustrated in Figure 1.1.

Figure 1.1. *The R&D agenda for visual analytics addresses needs for innovation in interrelated research areas.*

Analytical Reasoning (Chapter 2)

Analytical reasoning techniques are the method by which users obtain deep insights that directly support situation assessment, planning, and decision making. Visual analytics must facilitate high-quality human judgment with a limited investment of the analysts' time. Visual analytics tools must enable diverse analytical tasks such as

- Understanding past and present situations quickly, as well as the trends and events that have produced current conditions
- Identifying possible alternative futures and their warning signs
- Monitoring current events for emergence of warning signs as well as unexpected events
- Determining indicators of the intent of an action or an individual
- Supporting the decision maker in times of crisis.

These tasks will be conducted through a combination of individual and collaborative analysis, often under extreme time pressure. Visual analytics must enable hypothesis-based and scenario-based analytical techniques, providing support for the analyst to reason based on the available evidence. Visual analytics must help the analyst discover the unexpected, whether by detecting unexpected relationships or showing that expected relationships are missing. Visual analytics must also focus on capturing the discoveries and the results of the analytic process and on making them available to others as a basis for future understanding.

Visual Representations and Interaction Techniques (Chapter 3)

Visual representations and interaction techniques take advantage of the human eye's broad bandwidth pathway into the mind to allow users to see, explore, and understand large amounts of information at once. Information visualization research has focused on the creation of approaches for conveying abstract information in intuitive ways. Visual analytics must build upon this research base to create visual representations that instantly convey the important content of information, within context. This visual representation is essential to the analytical reasoning process.

There is no single visual metaphor that can meet all analytical needs. A suite of visual metaphors and associated visual approaches is necessary to provide users with multiple complementary views of their information. Analysts must have the capability to tailor these visual tools to fit their task and their individual analytical style. Approaches are needed to visually represent dynamic data of all types. These representations must be able to convey changing conditions and situational assessments as events transpire, analytical understanding evolves, and requirements change.

Visual representations alone cannot satisfy analytical needs. Interaction techniques are required to support the dialogue between the analyst and the data. While basic interactions such as search techniques are common in software today, more sophisticated interactions are also needed to support the analytical reasoning process. A strong foundation must be developed for interaction science to enable researchers to develop the best interaction techniques to support any given task, timescale, and interaction environment.

Data Representations and Transformations (Chapter 4)

Data are at the heart of the analytical challenge. Analytically important data are buried in vast streams of all types. These data, in their raw form, are rarely appropriate for direct analysis. The key challenge is to create data representations and transformations that convert all types of conflicting and dynamic data into forms that facilitate analytical understanding. These representations must support varying levels of abstraction to facilitate the analysis of massive and dynamic data collections, at multiple scales, and within multiple contexts. Data representations must represent data context where known, but they also must appropriately represent information that is lacking context, incomplete, and uncertain. Today, data are generally analyzed within a collection of a similar data type. Visual analytics must bring all relevant information into a single consistent analytical context, regardless of the form in which the information began, to support analysis and discovery.

Production, Presentation, and Dissemination (Chapter 5)

To have impact, the results of an analysis must be communicated accurately to others. Production of analytical outputs, assembly of presentations appropriate for different audiences, and dissemination of analytical results are essential steps in the analytical process. Results must be communicated to numerous audiences, from policymakers to the general population, in unambiguous and meaningful ways. New approaches are needed to simplify the production of analytical assessments, so that presentations of results, relevant facts and evidence, and associated uncertainties can be assembled rapidly to fit the needs of different audiences. These results must be communicated within the context of the receiver and at the appropriate level of detail to meet their needs.

Moving Research into Practice (Chapter 6)

Supporting these research areas are four important areas that must be addressed to accelerate the often tortuous path from research into practice.

Evaluation. Visual analytics must address methods for evaluating whether or not a particular tool or technique is truly having a positive impact. Usability evaluation, while valuable, is insufficient. Visual analytics must develop meaningful and effective techniques to evaluate the actual value any specific visual analytic technique may provide. Sterile test conditions can often produce different evaluation results than would be observed in actual analytical practice. We must develop evaluation approaches and test data sets that give the best possible indicators of true value in an analyst's hands.

Privacy and Security. Analysts work with information drawn from multiple sources, each of which has associated security and privacy constraints. Laws exist that govern how information may be used and combined, and those laws must underpin visual analytics approaches. Tools must proactively adopt and support approaches such as data anonymization, data minimization, audit trails, and access controls to both protect privacy and ensure information security.

System Interoperability. System interoperability issues are central to the successful research, evaluation, and ultimate deployment of visual analytics tools. Visual analytics tools will be developed by disparate groups, yet they must successfully complement one another in a single seamless analytical environment. Interoperability must be considered at every step in the R&D process, from sharing of research-level code to evaluation of tool suites developed by multiple teams. Visual analytics tools will be deployed in diverse application environments, and they must be engineered to permit flexible implementations that can fit within a variety of application architectures.

Technology Insertion. Technology insertion is the successful transition of a technology into widespread analytical use. This technology transfer process must be planned explicitly. We must understand how new visual analytics techniques fit into the user's overall analytic software environment as well as how they fit into the user's processes. We must define the training paths that help users understand how best to use a new technology and integrate it into their practices.

Fully addressing the research needs described in this agenda will require the concerted efforts of multidisciplinary teams of experts from throughout academia, industry, government, and the national laboratory system. It is imperative to expand the core group of researchers who are addressing these problems. To expand this talent base will require establishing formal educational opportunities for researchers, including educational outreach programs and development of new curricula. Through a set of coordinated research efforts, partnerships, and educational efforts, we can mobilize the research community to address these needs now and in the years to come. Chapter 7 describes the set of initiatives necessary to position the field of visual analytics for enduring success and issues the call to action to accomplish this agenda.

References

Alberts B and WA Wulf. 2002. *Making the Nation Safer: The Role of Science and Technology in Countering Terrorism*. National Academy of Sciences, Washington, D.C.

Department of Homeland Security. 2004. *Securing our Homeland: U.S. Department of Homeland Security Strategic Plan*. Available at http://www.dhs.gov/interweb/assetlibrary/DHS_StratPlan_FINAL_spread.pdf.

Eick S and A Karr. 2002. "Visual Scalability." *Journal of Computational and Graphical Statistics* 11(1):22-43.

Hennessy JL, DA Patterson, and HS Lin, eds. 2003. *Information Technology for Counterterrorism: Immediate Actions and Future Possibilities*. National Academy of Sciences, Washington, D.C.

Lyman P and HR Varian. 2003. "How Much Information?" Available at http://www.sims.berkeley.edu/how-much-info.

Munzner T, F Guimbretiere, S Tasiran, L Zhang, and Y Zhou. 2003. "TreeJuxtaposer: Scalable Tree Comparison Using Focus+Context with Guaranteed Visibility." *ACM Transactions on Graphics: Special Issue Proceedings of ACM SIGGRAPH 2003* 22(3):453-462.

National Commission on Terrorist Attacks. 2004. *The 9/11 Commission Report*. W.W. Norton and Company, Ltd., New York.

"It is not enough to have a good mind. The main thing is to use it well."

—Rene Descartes, *Discourse on Method*, 1637

The Science of Analytical Reasoning

When we create a mental picture, speak of the mind's eye, say "I see" to indicate understanding, or use many other vision-based metaphors, we are expressing the innate connection among vision, visualization, and our reasoning processes. This chapter describes the work needed to put this deep realization onto a useful scientific foundation backed by theory, predictive models, and evaluations.

This science of analytical reasoning provides the reasoning framework upon which one can build both strategic and tactical visual analytics technologies for threat analysis, prevention, and response. Analytical reasoning is central to the analyst's task of applying human judgments to reach conclusions from a combination of evidence and assumptions.

Visual analytics strives to facilitate the analytical reasoning process by creating software that maximizes human capacity to perceive, understand, and reason about complex and dynamic data and situations. It must build upon an understanding of the reasoning process, as well as an understanding of underlying cognitive and perceptual principles, to provide mission-appropriate interactions that allow analysts to have a true discourse with their information. The goal is to facilitate high-quality human judgment with a limited investment of the analysts' time.

In emergency management and border security contexts, analytical reasoning provides the foundation for the abstraction of data at multiple levels to convey the right information at the right time and place. It provides the principles for conveying context-appropriate information that can be cascaded to all levels of an organization to support rapid decision making.

Analytical reasoning must be a richly collaborative process and must adhere to principles and models for collaboration. Collaborative analysis provides both the human and computational scalability necessary to support reasoning, assessment, and action.

The science of analytical reasoning underpins the research areas described in the rest of this book. It provides a basis and a direction for the science of visual representations and interactions described in Chapter 3. It forms a foundation for the principles of depicting information in meaningful and novel visual representations.

The integration of interaction at a basic level in perceptual and cognitive theory will explain and empower interactive visualizations, which are fundamentally different from static visualizations and are essential to visual analytics tools. The focus on analytic discourse and reasoning processes will make visual representations relevant, focused, and effective. The data representations and transformations described in Chapter 4 must be informed by the needs to support the creation of interactive visualizations from massive and complex data and to represent higher-level concepts, such as levels of abstraction. These representations and transformations must also support the capture of both intermediate and final products of the analytical process. Analytical reasoning principles must inform the research in production, presentation, and dissemination described in Chapter 5, so that the resulting communications can be clear and on point. As illustrated in Chapter 6, the science of analytical reasoning provides a practical basis for evaluation of visual analytics tools, as well as important insights about the training and user support necessary to facilitate adoption of these tools in analytical environments.

This chapter begins with an overview of the analysis process and its products, from the point of view of the practitioner. We then discuss the concept of analytic discourse, which is the interactive, computer-mediated process of applying human judgment to assess an issue. This discourse is at the core of the analytical process and is integral to threat analysis, emergency response, and borders and infrastructure protection. Analytic discourse represents an applied research approach to the analytic reasoning challenge. Next, we describe sense-making, which provides a more theoretical basis for understanding the reasoning process based on models of human information processing. Sense-making is both a working analysis approach and a possible framework for a broader theory of analytical reasoning and human-information discourse. Next, we discuss the foundational perceptual and cognitive theory and models that provide the grounding for visual analytics tools that support the analytical reasoning process. We conclude with a discussion of the theoretical basis for successful collaborative visual analytics. Such collaboration must extend the principles of visual analytics to environments where humans and machines reason together intimately regardless of whether or not they are separated by time or distance.

An Overview of Analysis

The goal of visual analytics is to create software systems that will support the analytical reasoning process. This section describes the process and language of the analysis process from the practitioner's perspective and describes the intermediate and final products of the analytical reasoning process.

The Analysis Process

Analysis is both an art and a science. The goal of analysis is to make judgments about an *issue*, or larger question. Analyses are often done on smaller questions relating to a larger issue. Analysts must often reach their judgments under significant time pressure and with limited and conflicting information. Their judgments necessarily reflect their best understanding of a situation, complete with assumptions, supporting evidence, and uncertainties. Analytical outcomes are documented in the form of a *product*, which is a tangible result of an analysis that can be shared with others.

Analysis is necessary to support identification of threats and vulnerabilities, protection of borders and critical infrastructure, and emergency preparation and response. Analysts may be asked to perform several different types of tasks, depending upon the requester's needs:

- *Assess* – Understand the current world around them and explain the past. The product of this type of analysis is an *assessment*.
- *Forecast* – Estimate future capabilities, threats, vulnerabilities, and opportunities.
- *Develop Options* – Establish different optional reactions to potential events and assess their effectiveness and implications. For homeland security issues in particular, analysts may develop options to defend against, avert, or disrupt threats. In emergency response situations, analysis is used to understand response options and their implications.

Regardless of the type of analysis, analysts make judgments from evidence and assumptions using reasoning. They seek and process a set of information, ideally from multiple sources; assert and test key assumptions; and build knowledge structures using estimation and inferential techniques to form chains of reasoning that *articulate and defend* judgments on the issue [Chen, 2003; Clark & Brennan, 1991].

The term *defend* suggests that the reasoning, evidence, level of certainty, key gaps, and alternatives are made clear. Defensible judgments enable effective collaboration, review, and communication. They also support the comparison of conclusions drawn from alternative techniques. The analysis practices used and standards for their application, including checks and balances to ensure thorough consideration of options, are collectively referred to as *tradecraft* [CIA, 1997].

Analysis is an iterative process. Not only is the process of reaching judgment about a single question often an iterative one, but obtaining that answer produces several more questions, leading to additional analyses about the larger issue.

Analysis is also a collaborative process. Information, including judgments and written products, are shared among analysts working on related problems. Research issues associated with supporting this collaboration are discussed later in this chapter. Collaboration must be conducted with full adherence to security and privacy laws and policies. Security and privacy issues are discussed in more depth in Chapter 6.

Steps in the Analytical Process

The analytical process is structured and disciplined. Depending on time availability and task complexity, it is often an iterative process. The analyst's solution process begins with planning. He or she must determine how to address the issue that has been posed, what resources to use, and how to allocate time to various parts of the process to meet deadlines. Next, the analyst must gather information containing the relevant evidence and become familiar with it, and incorporate it with the knowledge he or she already has. The analyst next generates multiple candidate explanations, often in the form of hypotheses. The analyst evaluates these alternative explanations in light of evidence and assumptions to reach a judgment about the most likely explanations or outcomes. Once conclusions have been reached, good analytical practice dictates that the analyst engage in processes to broaden his or her thinking to include other explanations that were not previously considered.

At the conclusion of the analysis, the analyst creates reports, presentations, or other products that summarize the analytical judgments. These products are reviewed extensively in a collaborative process. Then they are shared with the requesters of information and with other audiences as appropriate. These products summarize the judgments made and the supporting reasoning that was developed during the analytical process. The subject of production, presentation, and dissemination of results is addressed in more depth in Chapter 5.

A detailed discussion of the intelligence cycle, or knowledge management process within which the analytic endeavor exists, is beyond the scope of this chapter but can be found in Tenet [1999] and Waltz [2003].

This analysis process is important to a wide variety of homeland security needs. Desk analysts predominantly address the analysis of threats and vulnerabilities. Their careers focus on daily practice of these analytical techniques. Border and infrastructure protection requires analytic effort to understand and respond to evolving situations. Emergency management personnel, whether first responders or personnel coordinating the response, pursue similar goals in order to identify and take appropriate actions. In emergency response contexts, however, the time available for analysis is generally shorter, meaning that the analysis cannot be as thorough, and the results must be converted directly into action.

Regardless of the situation, executing sound analysis routinely is challenging. This is further complicated by the fact that the pool of experienced analysts is limited. As Richards Heuer illustrates in his key work, *Psychology of Intelligence Analysis* [1999], analytical processes can compensate for human limitations in managing complex and fluid problems.

Analytic Reasoning Artifacts

The analyst collects and organizes information as he or she progresses toward judgment about a question. Throughout the reasoning process, the analyst identifies or creates tangible pieces of information that contribute to reaching defensible judgments. We refer to these pieces of information here as *reasoning artifacts. Products* can be thought of as reasoning artifacts that are meant to be shared with others to convey the results of the analysis. A description of common analytical reasoning artifacts appears in Table 2.1.

Table 2.1. Common reasoning artifacts.

Elemental artifacts: artifacts derived from isolated pieces of information	
Source Intelligence	An individual piece of intelligence (e.g., a document, photograph, signal, sensor reading) that has come to the analyst's attention through a collection or retrieval activity.
Relevant Information	Source intelligence that is believed to be relevant to the issue and usable for constructing arguments and judgments.
Assumption	An asserted fact, and its basis, that will be used for reasoning. Assumptions must be managed separately from evidence, as sound practice demands their critical inspection. An assumption may come from the analyst's prior knowledge, an earlier conclusion or product of an analysis, or a key, presently unknowable presumed fact that allows judgment to progress despite a gap in knowledge.
Evidence	The information or assumption takes on argument value when the analyst assesses its quality, accuracy, strength, certainty, and utility against higher-level knowledge artifacts such as hypotheses and scenarios. Assessing the utility can be as simple as judging if the evidence is consistent or inconsistent with a hypothesis or scenario or if the evidence argues for or against an inference.
Pattern artifacts: artifacts derived from collections of information	
Patterns and Structure	Relationships among many pieces of data to form evidence. Analysts often create tables, charts, and networks of data to detect and extract pattern or structure.
Temporal and Spatial Patterns	Temporal relationships and spatial patterns that may be revealed through timelines and maps. Changes in pattern, surprising events, coincidences, and anomalous timing may all lead to evidence recognition. The simple act of placing information on a timeline or a map can generate clarity and profound insight.
Higher-order knowledge constructs	
Arguments	Logical inferences linking evidence and other reasoning artifacts into defensible judgments of greater knowledge value. Extensive formal systems, such as predicate calculus, give a solid inferential basis.
Causality	Specialized inference about time, argument, and evidence that makes the argument that an event or action caused a second event or action. Causality is often critical to assessments. It is also a source of many biases and errors, and demands careful review.
Models of Estimation	A means of encoding a complex problem by understanding logic and applying it to evidence, resulting in a higher-level judgment that estimates the significance of available evidence to the issue at hand. Some important classes of models are utility models (which estimate the value of a potential action to an actor using multiple weighted criteria), indicator models (used to estimate if outcomes of interest may be in the process of development), behavioral models (of individual and group dynamics), economic models, and physical models. Specialized analytic activity may involve research using models, simulation, and gaming. A repertoire of basic problem modeling and structuring techniques is invaluable to the analyst.
Complex reasoning constructs	
Hypothesis	A conjectured explanation, assessment, or forecast that should be supported by the evidence.
Scenarios or Scenario Fragments	Sequences of information with "story" value in explaining or defending part of a judgment chain. For example, a threat scenario might address a target, method, actor, motive, means, and opportunity.

These artifacts range from the very simplest pieces of raw data to the highest-level constructs that represent large parts of the analytic solution. The most complex constructs, such as hypotheses and scenarios, are used primarily to help structure the available knowledge, facilitate its articulation and delivery in product, test the completeness of the knowledge, and identify if additional knowledge or explanatory paths may be required.

Hypotheses and scenarios are used to express and explain a large collection of evidence, so they are valuable both as reasoning aids and to support the process of conducting competing evaluations. For example, the technique of alternative competing hypothesis evaluation [Garfinkel, 1967] highlights the value of retaining competing hypotheses and seeking evidence that refutes hypotheses, or, even better, diagnostic evidence that supports one hypothesis but refutes another, to select the hypothesis that best explains the evidence.

Analytic Discourse

The analytical reasoning process described above forms the basis for the ongoing dialogue between analysts and their information. Enabling this discourse is at the heart of the visual analytics mission. This section describes the relationship of this discourse to the analysis process and recommends steps for advancing the state of the art in analytic discourse.

A Definition of Analytic Discourse

Analytic discourse is the technology-mediated dialogue between an analyst and his or her information to produce a judgment about an issue. This discourse is an iterative and evolutionary process by which a path is built from definition of the issue to the assembly of evidence and assumptions to the articulation of judgments.

The analyst's information includes:

- The issue being addressed. At the outset, the analyst refines his or her understanding of the question to be answered, sometimes broadening or adjusting the scope so as to respond to the question that was intended, rather than what was explicitly asked.
- Information that the analyst has gathered regarding the issue, which may or may not include relevant evidence. Through exploration and investigation, the analyst identifies and evaluates evidence within the available data and requests additional data as needed.
- The analyst's evolving knowledge about the issue, including assumptions, hypotheses, scenarios, models, or arguments.

In an analytic discourse, the strengths of both the computer system and the human are harnessed to improve the analysis process. The computer finds patterns in information and organizes the information in ways that are meant to be revealing to the analyst. The analyst supplies his or her knowledge in ways that help the computer refine and organize information more appropriately.

Analytic discourse should support the goal of creating a product that articulates a defensible judgment in problems of assessment, forecasting, and planning. Effective solutions will require a true dialogue, mediated by technology, among the user, information, issue, and evolving judgment.

Supporting Analysis Through Analytic Discourse

It should be the goal of visual analytics systems to support the analyst in *executing sound analytic technique routinely*, facilitating insight and sound judgment in time-pressured environments and compensating for inexperience wherever possible. An effective analytic discourse must accommodate the unique characteristics of the analysis process, some of which are described here.

Analysis is generally not a linear process. Analysts spend time engaged in *convergent thinking*, which involves assembling evidence to find an answer, and *divergent thinking*, which involves thinking creatively to ensure that plausible alternatives have not been overlooked. Many analysts engage in controlled broadening checks during their investigations, during which they consider the broader context of the issue and examine alternative explanations and data that do not fit with their current reasoning. Therefore, visual analytics systems must facilitate this iterative and nonlinear process through an active discourse.

People cannot reason effectively about hypotheses and scenarios that are unavailable to them [Garfinkel, 1967]. Key to good analytic discipline is early identification of competing explanations and chains of reasoning for the issue under study. Awareness of the competing ideas must be maintained actively, so that they are kept "alive" as analytic possibilities. Often the most plausible explanation will be researched extensively, but a thorough check is to always revisit the key alternative ideas and ask, "If I were wrong, how would I know?" Visual analytics tools must facilitate the analyst's task of actively considering competing hypotheses.

Another important analytic technique is the enumeration and testing of assumptions. Explicit representation of these assumptions facilitates this process. Additional analytical techniques include consideration of biases that may have precluded consideration of important alternatives, sensitivity to potential deception in evidence, and in cases of high risk, devil's advocacy processes that assume a differing interpretation of data and attempt to reason in that direction, exposing potential weaknesses in the product. These techniques are examples of structured ways to review the product and its supporting evidence and reasoning, and they can be greatly facilitated by a visual analytics system.

Analysis products are expected to clearly communicate the assessment or forecast, the evidence on which it is based, knowledge gaps or unknowns, the analyst's degree of certainty in the judgment, and any significant alternatives and their indicators. Visual analytics systems must capture this information and facilitate its presentation in ways that meet the needs of the recipient of the information.

These tools and techniques also must allow analysts to look at their problem at multiple levels of abstraction and support reasoning about situations that change over time, sometimes very rapidly.

Supporting Analyst Operations on Reasoning Artifacts

Analytic discourse must support a full range of operations to derive, manipulate, and understand reasoning artifacts. For simple elemental and pattern artifacts, visual analytics tools must support data retrieval, navigation, and discovery operations to permit data collection or foraging. For higher-level knowledge artifacts such as arguments, causality, and estimative modeling, visual analytics tools must support construction or formulation operations.

Analytic discourse must permit the analyst to create abstractions of these artifacts. That is, it must be possible to obtain a simpler representation of the information that is more suitable for the product or collaboration.

Analysts often want to compare knowledge artifacts to find similarities and differences in evidence, arguments, or hypotheses. The analysis process often demands that an argument, hypothesis, or scenario be challenged or tested to find weaknesses and inconsistencies. During the collaborative creation of a product, it is often critical to frame the questions being addressed in terms of the evidence and reasoning rather then in terms of a conclusion.

Visual analytics systems must support all of these needs to enable true analytic discourse.

State of the Art

Much has been done to study and document simple and effective analysis techniques. References such as *The Thinker's Toolkit* [Jones, 1995], *Conceptual Blockbusting* [Adams, 2001], and *Psychology of Intelligence Analysis* [Heuer, 1999] describe representative approaches. The professional analyst is often armed with a broad repertoire of techniques, but these are not available to the research community as a whole.

Analysts must deal with data that are dynamic, incomplete, often deceptive, and evolving. The problem of coping with such diverse and changing information has been recognized for centuries. Descartes [1637] described a problem-solving method wherein data are analyzed, broken into their elements, and studied to reveal evidence, and solutions are synthesized by accumulating the evidence. For the researcher, the concept of allowing the breakdown of information and its assembly to solutions remains an interesting one. For example, a single piece of source information (e.g., document or photograph) may contribute many different pieces of evidence to understanding and may support or refute many differing and competing hypotheses.

Methods of evidence navigation and discovery from available information collections, even ones of a practical scale in the problem areas of homeland security, are rapidly maturing. Retrieval technology is very mature; Boolean retrieval is universally in practice; and more advanced forms of retrieval, such as natural language question answering for simple facts, are maturing. Extraction technology, to isolate entities and relationships within text, is maturing, with entity extraction commonly used.

There is an excellent body of science, some in service, to support the visualization and navigation of information spaces of up to one million documents or so. There are mature capabilities to support basic analytic discourse, but work needs to be done to expand the ability to respond to the analyst's more sophisticated problem-solving goals. Much work remains to be done to extend these techniques to accommodate the massive scale and dynamic nature of visual analytics tasks.

Many mathematical techniques exist for representing pattern and structure, as well as visualizing correlations, time patterns, metadata relationships, and networks of linked information. For simple patterns and structure they work well; for more complex reasoning tasks—particularly temporal reasoning and combined time and space reasoning—much work remains to be done. The existing techniques also fail when faced with the massive scale, rapidly changing data, and variety of information types we expect for visual analytics tasks.

Structured argumentation, which is the linking of evidence and assumptions through formal logic, has a large literature to draw on (see, for example, Schum [1994]). Some capabilities for structured argumentation are in limited practice, and a good basic body of research has been conducted. Kirschner [2003] summarizes current views of the relationship between visualization and argumentation. It is often speculated that structured argumentation could be the basis of visual analytics systems. More work is needed to explore this possibility. One concern is that formalized systems trend towards interaction that lacks the approachability, fluidity, and speed needed for effective application.

In hypothesis formulation and testing, and in models of inference, there is considerable science as well—some from the artificial intelligence and ontological modeling communities, and some from epistemology. Some promising science demonstration systems have been developed to generate and track hypotheses, but this research remains a longer-term goal for effective, tractable application.

Current techniques break down when composite reasoning processes—that is, the joining of many types of reasoning artifacts—are in use; when the problem demands harmonizing many different insights from differing artifacts; and when the ability to retain active competitive explanations, such as during suspected deception, is critical.

Current techniques also break down when applied to the massive and dynamic multi-type data common to the homeland security arena, as described in Chapter 1. Another area of weakness in existing science is that once an important piece of evidence is recognized or an inference is made, it is often exceedingly difficult to capture and record the progress directly, forcing reliance on memory, notes, or annotations. Likewise, a sudden recognition, question, or insight usually cannot be recorded without disrupting the ongoing analysis context. Visual analytics software can and should maintain records of progress for the analyst as an intrinsic byproduct of engaging in the discourse.

An integrated science for analytic discourse does not yet exist, but its creation will offer tremendous benefits to analysts and the homeland security missions.

Technology Needs

To develop an integrated science for analytic discourse, we recommend two initial actions.

Recommendation 2.1

Refine our understanding of reasoning artifacts and develop knowledge representations to capture, store, and reuse the knowledge generated throughout the entire analytic process.

These knowledge representations will primarily be used to support interoperation among software tools used to support analytic discourse. These knowledge representations must retain the reasoning artifacts that are produced throughout the analytical process, as well as retain the judgment chains and links to supporting information associated with each analytical product. It must provide the mapping between the reasoning artifact and the original data used to produce it, along with information about both data quality and method of derivation for the reasoning artifact.

Recommendation 2.2

Develop visually based methods to support the entire analytic reasoning process, including the analysis of data as well as structured reasoning techniques such as the construction of arguments, convergent-divergent investigation, and evaluation of alternatives. These methods must support not only the analytical process itself but also the progress tracking and analytical review processes.

The challenge of integrating the entire range of activity described here, in a manner that is usable, understandable, and time-efficient to the analyst, is substantial. We must enable not only the analytic processes that an individual follows to reach a judgment but also the communication processes that are necessary both to track the progress of the analytical process and to share the results of the analysis and supporting information to facilitate reviews.

Sense-Making Methods

While the concept of analytic discourse represents a more applied research perspective, research in sense-making provides a theoretical basis for understanding many of the analytical reasoning tasks that the analyst performs.

Many analytical reasoning tasks follow a process of

- Information gathering
- Re-representation of the information in a form that aids analysis
- Development of insight through the manipulation of this representation
- Creation of some knowledge product or direct action based on the knowledge insight.

As illustrated in Figure 2.1, these activities may be repeated and may come out of order, although there is the notion of an overall cycle. We call tasks that follow this sort of pattern *sense-making tasks* or sometimes *knowledge crystallization tasks*.

Examples abound in commerce, education, research, military activities, and intelligence. For example, consider the sense-making process involved in choosing which model of laptop computer to purchase. The shopper may *gather information* from magazines and the internet. The information collected may be *re-represented* by creating a table of computer models by attributes. This representation may be *manipulated*, deleting rows of attributes for serial and parallel ports, for example, and adding new rows for FireWire and graphics accelerators. The shopper gains insight into her choice by inspecting the matrix, possibly by rearranging the rows and columns, or highlighting cells. The *knowledge product* in this case is a rationalized purchase decision.

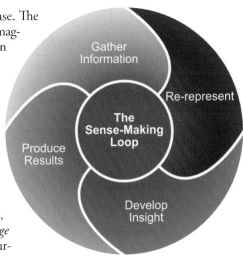

Figure 2.1. *The analytical reasoning process.*

State of the Art

Some variant of this sense-making process is often encountered in the analysis of information-intensive tasks. For example, Lederberg [1989] describes the scientific process as a sort of sense-making cycle with multiple feedbacks. The CIA [1995], in a report on the need for visualization, discusses intelligence analysis essentially as a sense-making loop of collection tasking, data monitoring, interpretation and analysis, drafting/editing, and customer support. Card et al. [1999] frame information visualization using the concept of a sense-making loop. Recent work has suggested a similar sense-making loop cycle (Figure 2.2, adapted from Pirolli & Card, 2005) for some types of analysis work. Boxes in the diagram represent data and arrows represent processes. An analyst filters message traffic and actively searches for information, collecting it in an information store (called a *shoebox* in the diagram). Relevant snippets from this store are extracted from these documents into evidence files, which may be simply text files in a word processing program. Information from the evidence may be represented in some schema, or a conceptual form into which information is transformed for exploration and manipulation, and from which it is translated to produce briefings and other products. Schemas may take the form of representations such as timelines, or they may simply reflect the internalized mental representations of the expert. The evidence thus laid out may be cast into hypotheses or methods of structured reasoning. Finally, information is transformed into an output knowledge product, such as a briefing or a report. This is an expansion of the process we saw in the laptop example above: the information is gathered, mapped into some set of core representations that encapsulate the heart of the knowledge domain and where operators on the knowledge are enabled, then transformed into the knowledge product.

The process is not a straight progression but can have many loops. For example, construction of an evidence file can evoke the need to go back and collect new evidence. Among the many possible loops, there are two especially important ones: an information

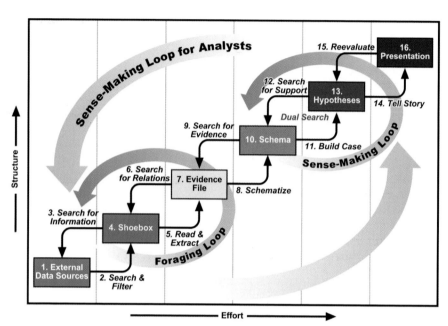

Figure 2.2. *Nominal sense-making loop for some types of intelligence analysts.*

foraging loop, which focuses on the gathering and processing of data to create schemas, and the sense-making loop, which includes the processes involved in moving from schemas to finished products.

Other researchers have come to a similar conclusion about the nature of sense-making for intelligence analysts and first responders. For example, Klein [2004] has a data/frame-based theory of sense-making, which plays a similar role to *schema* in Figure 2.2. For Klein, a frame is a mental structure that organizes the data and sense-making is the process of fitting information into that frame. Frames are a consequence of developed expertise. Bodnar [2003] describes a process similar to Figure 2.2 in his book on warning analysis for intelligence.

Effects of time scale on sense-making

Sense-making has been studied from more varied points of view than the intelligence analysis process described in Figure 2.2. Leedom [2001], for example, has reviewed this field with respect to its relevance to military decision making. The sense-making process is affected by the time scale for the process and whether the process involves individuals or organizations.

At the organizational level and operating on a time scale of months and years, Weick [1995] claims that the social dynamics of organizational processes are based on sense-making. A set of "mental minimal sensible structures" together with goals lead to the creation of situational understanding and direction for members of organizations.

In situations that require action within minutes or hours, Klein [1989, 1998] has developed a model of recognition-primed decision making, as part of a program on naturalistic decision making that has been used as the basis of military command and control. This model emphasizes the role of the knowledge structures built from expertise and experience in allowing a soldier or a firefighter to make sense of a situation and rapidly formulate an action. The lack of some expected features of a situation can also trigger sense-making and action.

In cases where action is required within seconds or minutes, Endsley [1995] and others have studied the notion of *situational awareness* for individuals, particularly in the context of advanced cockpit displays for combat air tasks. Situational awareness is the perception of the elements in the environment within a volume of space and time; comprehension of their meaning; the projection of their status into the near future; and the prediction of how various actions will affect the fulfillment of one's goals.

It thus contains a cycle of perception, comprehension, projection, and prediction. A related action-oriented cycle is Boyd's Observation-Orientation-Decision-Action loop [1987]. Although Boyd was a combat Air Force pilot and his ideas derive from the time pressure of combat, he generalized them to strategizing taking place over days and months by organizations.

Models of sense-making and its cost structure

Each of the processes of sense-making, from finding and extracting information to re-representing it for analysis, to creating an end product, has a cost. Costs could be thought of in terms of time investment, level of difficulty, or resources required, for example. The collective costs and gains of the individual sense-making processes are referred to as its *cost structure*. The cost structure may strongly shape the behavior of the user.

The cost structure of the lower end of the sense-making loop in Figure 2.2 has been addressed in work on information foraging theory [Pirolli & Card, 1999]. The cost structure is characterized in terms of information gain and costs (usually measured in time) for obtaining and consuming the information. A reasonable model is that the user will seek to adapt to the information environment to maximize information gains per unit cost. Predictions can be made about what sorts of information users will exploit and when users will decide to move from one patch of information to another.

Other models have been developed to represent user strategies for sense-making. Patterson et al. [2001] show how intelligence analysts in a simulated situation trade off between widening the search for documents ("explore"), narrowing it ("enrich"), and reading documents ("exploit") and how these relate to missed information (Figure 2.3). In general, they show that techniques for handling

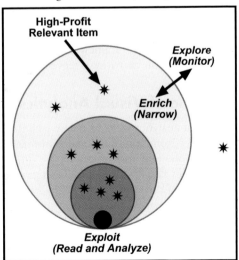

Figure 2.3. Circles show the space of documents being considered. Stars indicate relevant documents. Analysts adjust their activities among exploring, enriching, and exploiting documents.

context are a key to coping with high information loads [Woods et al., 2002].

Russell et al. [1993] have described sense-making in terms of a "learning loop complex" (Figure 2.4). First is a search for a good representation (the generation loop). Then there is an attempt to encode information in the representation (the data coverage loop). The attempt at encoding information in the representation identifies items that do not fit ("residue"). This gives rise to an attempt to adjust the representation so that it has better coverage (the "representation shift loop"). The result is a more compact representation of the essence of the information relative to the intended task.

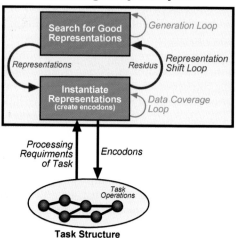

Figure 2.4. Learning Loop Complex theory of sense-making.

Another source of theory for the sense-making process comes from the study of scientific discovery [Shrager & Langley, 1990; Klahr, 2000]. An important theoretical concept is the Scientific Discovery through Dual Search (SDDS) model. This model emphasizes that sense-making or discovery in science often involves an alternating dual search both through a problem space of hypotheses and through a problem space of data. Sometimes it is easier to make progress by looking for explanations of data by generating hypotheses; other times it is easier to make progress by creating experiments to generate data to test hypotheses. The SDDS model was proposed as a general framework for behavior in any scientific reasoning task. The full set of possible activities is represented in Figure 2.5.

The Role of Visual Analytics in Sense-Making

Visual analytics seeks to marry techniques from information visualization with techniques from computational transformation and analysis of data. Information visualization itself forms part of the direct interface between user and machine. Information visualization amplifies human cognitive capabilities in six basic ways (Table 2.2) [Card et al., 1999]: 1) by *increasing cognitive resources*, such as by using a visual resource to expand human working memory, 2) by *reducing search*, such as by representing a large amount of data in a small space, 3) by *enhancing the recognition of patterns*, such as when information is organized in space by its time relationships, 4) by *supporting the easy perceptual inference of relationships* that are otherwise more difficult to induce, 5) by *perceptual monitoring* of a large number of potential events, and 6) by *providing a manipulable medium* that, unlike static diagrams, enables the exploration of a space of parameter values.

These capabilities of information visualization, combined with computational data analysis, can be applied to analytic reasoning to support the sense-making process.

Visual analytics could be used to facilitate any point along the sense-making cycle, such as accelerated search, accelerated reading, accelerated extracting and linking, schema visualization, hypothesis management and structured argumentation, or interactive presentation. Visual analytics can enhance the scale or effectiveness of the analyst's schemas, not only for expert analysts but also—and especially—for those below the expert tier.

Visual analytics can reduce this cost structure associated with sense-making in two primary ways: 1) by transforming information into forms that allow humans to offload cognition onto easier perceptual processes or to otherwise expand human cognitive capacities as detailed in Table 2.2, and 2) by allowing software agents to do some of the filtering, representation translation, interpretation, and even reasoning.

Visual analytics systems can be developed starting from a notion of sense-making and adding computer-enhanced capabilities of visualization and data analytics. The ultimate goal is to produce a broader science of analytical reasoning built on the foundation of sense-making.

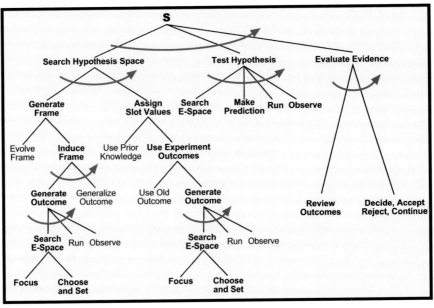

Figure 2.5. Klahr's SDDS theory of scientific discovery. The dual search through hypothesis and experiment problem spaces is represented here as an "and/or graph" of operations. Arrow arcs indicate all of the sub-operations that must be performed. For sub-operations without an arrow arc, only one needs to be performed.

Table 2.2. How information visualization amplifies cognition.

1. Increased resources	
High-bandwidth hierarchical interaction	The human moving gaze system partitions limited channel capacity so that it combines high spatial resolution and wide aperture in sensing the visual environments [Resnikoff, 1989].
Parallel perceptual processing	Some attributes of visualizations can be processed in parallel compared to text, which is serial.
Offload work from cognitive to perceptual system	Some cognitive inferences done symbolically can be recoded into inferences done with simple perceptual operations [Larkin & Simon, 1987].
Expanded working memory	Visualizations can expand the working memory available for solving a problem [Norman, 1993].
Expanded storage of information	Visualizations can be used to store massive amounts of information in a quickly accessible form (e.g., maps).
2. Reduced search	
Locality of processing	Visualizations group information used together, reducing search [Larkin & Simon, 1987].
High data density	Visualizations can often represent a large amount of data in a small space [Tufte, 1983].
Spatially-indexed addressing	By grouping data about an object, visualizations can avoid symbolic labels [Larkin & Simon, 1987].
3. Enhanced recognition of patterns	
Recognition instead of recall	Recognizing information generated by a visualization is easier than recalling that information by the user.
Abstraction and aggregation	Visualizations simplify and organize information, supplying higher centers with aggregated forms of information through abstraction and selective omission [Card et al., 1991; Resnikoff, 1989].
Visual schemata for organization	Visually organizing data by structural relationships (e.g., by time) enhances patterns.
Value, relationship, trend	Visualizations can be constructed to enhance patterns at all three levels [Bauer et al., 1999].
4. Perceptual inference	
Visual representations make some problems obvious	Visualizations can support a large number of perceptual inferences that are extremely easy for humans [Larkin & Simon, 1987].
Graphical computations	Visualizations can enable complex, specialized graphical computations [Hutchins, 1996].
5. Perceptual monitoring	
	Visualizations can allow for the monitoring of a large number of potential events if the display is organized so that these stand out by appearance or motion.
6. Manipulable medium	
	Unlike static diagrams, visualizations can allow exploration of a space of parameter values and can amplify user operations.

Technology Needs

Sense-making provides a basis for analytic discourse, but research is necessary to expand this foundation to provide the necessary theoretical grounding for visual analytics.

Recommendation 2.3

Characterize the sense-making process as applied to analytic discourse in terms of the sense-making loop or other constructs and identify leverage points that are opportunities for intervention. Identify laboratory analogs of these tasks for development and evaluation.

We need to know more about the nature of the sense-making loop. We need integrated characterizations of sense-making problems, the systems used, and the users. Such characterizations would, of course, include descriptive studies. Visual analytics systems that do not adequately take into account the context of the data and their use will likely fail. But descriptive studies alone are not adequate for system design. Task analysis of user problems needs to reveal the underlying problem drivers, the forces shaping user behavior, the pain points, and the bottlenecks. We need models and theories of the situations at hand that shape the design space and predict a likely design result. We also need to develop problem analogs that can be used in the laboratory for development and testing. Andries Sanders [1984] advocated a "back-to-back" testing philosophy in which laboratory tests to obtain control were paired with field studies to assess content validity. The ability to evaluate problem analogs in the laboratory is especially important for applications such as analysis and emergency response, where access to analysts and large-scale emergency response scenarios may be limited.

Taxonomies of task types and data types must be developed. Studies must identify bottlenecks associated with different tasks and data characteristics. For example, looking for the answer to something you know, such as troop strength at a given point at a certain time in the context of abundant data, is different from looking for the same information with sparse data, which is different still from looking for anomalies that signal something you don't know.

Recommendation 2.4

Identify and focus on core conceptual schemas and create visually based components that support the analytical reasoning tasks associated with these schemas.

Because schemas are so central to the sense-making process, great benefit can be gained by identifying the core conceptual schemas for the intended domains and to create analytic visualizations to support these schemas. Certain core needs will arise repeatedly, such as analysis of timelines. By creating components that support the major analytic tasks associated with each of these conceptual schemas, we can address a wide range of common problems.

Several techniques have already been explored for how to map out scientific literatures [Small & Griffith, 1974; Chen, 2003], techniques that could be used for analysis.

Explore paradigms of human-machine interaction that treat visual analytic systems as mixed initiative supervisory control systems.

Visual analytics systems will have semi-automated analytic engines and user-driven interfaces. Some of these will be mixed initiative systems, in which either the system or the user can initiate action and have independent access to information and possibly to direct action. These systems need to be studied with insights derived from supervisory control systems. For example, if we consider which system can initiate action, which has to ask permission of the other before action can be executed, which can interrupt the other when, and which has to inform the other that it has taken action, we can define dozens of possible paradigms.

Perception and Cognition

Visual analytics combines analytical reasoning with interactive visualization, both of which are subject to the strengths and limitations of human perceptual and cognitive abilities. Effective tools must build on a deep understanding of how people sense, reason, and respond.

Many of the driving problems in Chapter 1 concern managing and understanding the enormous data stream intrinsic to visual analytics. An important aspect of the science of analytical reasoning is to create ways to represent data in forms that afford interaction and enable thought processes to translate from data to information, information to meaning, and meaning to understanding. As Herbert Simon [1996] said, "Solving a problem simply means representing it so that the solution is obvious." There is a long history of work on interactive technologies for cognitive augmentation, a goal set by Vannevar Bush in his article "As We May Think" [1945] and first put into operation by Douglas Engelbart and colleagues at Stanford Research Institute [Spohrer & Englebart, 2004] and the Bootstrap Institute.

Other driving problems have to do with improving visual representation. Chapter 3 is devoted to the science of visual representation and includes a thorough discussion of the state of the art in that domain, including some of the underlying perceptual and cognitive principles that are applied today. These principles must be better understood and integrated with those principles supporting analysis and reasoning to create more complete models for visual analytics.

Human-information discourse is that state where the mechanics of accessing and manipulating the tools of visual analytics vanish into a seamless flow of problem solving. How to achieve this flow, and how to use it to produce the concrete products needed in all visual analytic domains, constitutes a major research challenge. The concept of *flow* has its roots in psychology; application of its principles to interactive systems has yet to be achieved.

A key problem for visual analytics arises from the limited abilities of human perception and cognition, e.g., limits on short-term memory. To get around these limits, we use external aids, as discussed in Norman's *Things That Make Us Smart*. Heuer [1999] says, "Only by using such external memory aids am I able to cope with the volume and complexity of the information I want to use." Visual analytics is just such an external aid. To achieve the flow of analytic discourse, we need to better understand the interaction between perception and cognition and how they are affected when we work with a dynamic external aid. In other words, it is the process of perception and cognition and our resulting interactions that updates our understanding.

To achieve this understanding, which is crucial for meeting the challenges posed in this agenda, perception and cognition research will draw from work in multiple disciplines, such as perceptual and cognitive psychology, neuroscience, cartography and geographic information science, cognitive science, human-computer interaction, design, and computing. Visual analytics research must build on this work to forge a new and fundamental bond with interactive visualization.

State of the Art

The traditional model for human performance is a simple three-stage process, where some stimulus, such as a pattern of light, is processed first by the perceptual system to create a mental representation. In the second stage, cognitive processes evaluate that representation, accessing memory of other representations or schemas, for example, leading to some decision about the nature of the event and any response it requires. Finally, in stage 3, some motor action may be taken based on the decision reached in stage 2. Perceptual principles based on this process have been applied extensively to interactive visualization, as discussed further in Chapter 3. This common conceptual breakdown of mental processing forms the basis for the mass of experimental studies in perception, where each trial of an experiment presents a stimulus that is perceived and understood by the subject and the resulting motor response recorded as data for analysis of the nature of their perceptual and cognitive processes. While this is a useful conceptual breakdown for task performance (and as a window into the traditional literature in these fields), it is less useful as a model in situations such as analytic discourse where perception, cognition, and action iterate in a continuous flow.

Interaction must be a central concept in both perceptual and cognitive models. Interaction provides the mechanism of communication among users, visualizations, and visualization systems; it broadens the perceptual and cognitive processes by controlling how information is considered, taking second and subsequent looks at information, and taking different perspectives on the same information. These are key components in reasoning, problem solving, and knowledge building. Most visual perception research directed to understanding and using visual information displays has focused on static display. Much of the power of today's visual analytic methods, however, comes from their support for dynamic interaction. But the science of analytical reasoning must go beyond this. Just as it recognizes that interactive visualizations are fundamentally different from static visualizations, it must recognize that analytical reasoning coupled with interactive visualization is fundamentally different.

While scientists who conduct laboratory experiments take care to have all of their subjects use a consistent strategy, in practice our perceptual experience interacts with cognitive processes at all levels, enabling us to vary our strategies to fit a given problem situation. Whereas empirical studies typically avoid giving subjects feedback on their performance, in real-world tasks we are able to assess our performance by perceiving the results of our actions. This guides our further action. We perceive the repercussions of our actions, which also recalibrates perception, ensuring that vision, hearing, and touch maintain their agreement with each other. If we are to build richly interactive environments that aid cognitive processing, we must understand not only the levels of perception and cognition but also the framework that ties them together in a dynamic loop of enactive, or action-driven, cognition that is the cognitive architecture of human-information processing.

The literature on human abilities can be characterized roughly into three groups: higher-order embodied, enactive, and distributed models such as those proposed by Gibson [1986] and Varela et al. [1991] that describe conceptually the nature of processing in real-world environments; the large mass of laboratory-based psychology studies that establish the basic bottlenecks in human abilities to perceive, attend, and process information; and relatively applied work such as Bertin [1982], Norman [1993], Wickens and Hollands [2000], and Ware [2004] that seeks to adapt the laboratory and conceptual work to interaction tasks and situations of use.

Within specific domains, there are excellent examples of work that integrate perceptual, cognitive, and analytical models. For example, research to optimize the design of cockpit displays has created models that integrate perception, cognition, and decision making [Zhang, 1997] with an explicit goal of "decision support to provide the right information, in the right way, and at the right time" [Taylor et al., 2002]. There has been extensive work in the area of cartography and geographic information science to understand how maps and graphics do more than "make data visible" but are "active instruments in the users' thinking process" [MacEachren & Kraak, 2001]. MacEachren's *How Maps Work* [1995] combines an understanding of visual perception and cognition (along with other cognitive theory) with a semiotic approach to visual representation to create an integrated model of map-based visualization.

Researchers in fields other than the analysis domain also have looked at perceptual and cognitive support for decision making. The fields of law and medicine both have "evidence-based" approaches [Patel et al., 1994; 1997] analogous to those used for analytical reasoning in intelligence applications.

The perceptual aspects of interaction with information displays have been addressed occasionally (e.g., Rheingans [1992]; Jones [2000]) and research agendas have pointed to both perceptual and cognitive implications of interaction as research challenges (e.g., MacEachren and Kraak [2001]; National Research Council [2003]). Limited progress has been made so far; thus, understanding the relationships between visual perception and user interaction with visual analytic displays represents an important challenge at the core of visual analytic theory.

Work relating to the perceptual and cognitive underpinnings of visual analytics must often be assembled from a range of conferences and journals within isolated academic disciplines. However, there are a number of recent journals and conferences that attempt to integrate work from a number of disciplines. *ACM Transactions on Applied Perception* is just such a journal (http://www.acm.org/tap). The Symposium on Applied Perception in Graphics and Visualization (http://isg.cs.tcd.ie/gap/) alternates between a vision conference, such as the European Conference on Visual Perception, and SIGGRAPH, with papers that apply perceptual science to the design of visual interfaces. The Workshop on Smart Graphics (http://www.smartgraphics.org/) attempts to bring together researchers from Computer Graphics, Visualization, Art & Graphics Design, Cognitive Psychology, and Artificial Intelligence for multiple perspectives on computer-generated graphics. An increased number of applied papers are appearing at vision conferences, most notably the annual Vision Sciences conference (http://www.vision-sciences.org/). At the cognitive end of the spectrum, recent interest in augmented cognition (http://www.augmentedcognition.org) examines methods for supporting cognitive processing with interactive technologies.

The temptation here is to concentrate on applied work, which is most accessible to the design practitioner. It is important, however, to recognize that the complexity of the representations, tasks, and activities of analytic discourse will require us to delve further into the more abstract conceptualization of human performance as well as into research into bottlenecks in human abilities derived from laboratory studies. We are aided in this effort by recent work in the more global structure of human information processing, the cognitive architecture of task performance. Pylyshyn's *Seeing and Visualizing, It's Not What You Think* [2003] provides one example of this level of analysis.

Technology Needs

The science of visual analytics must be built on a deep understanding of how people sense, reason, and respond. This understanding is essential if we are to create tools, systems, and processes that complement the strengths and compensate for the weaknesses of the human beings involved.

Previous research towards applying perceptual and cognitive principles to the design of interactive systems has identified many of the fundamental perceptual and cognitive limits of the human mind. These limits are important, as they can help identify bottlenecks in the use of tools for interaction, visualization, and analytic reasoning. However, our goal must go beyond the identification of limits to the creation of predictive models, which inspire entirely new approaches to the problems of visual analytics. Such models permit the narrowing and focusing of the design space, and they make tenable the problems of efficient design that would otherwise be intractable. The foundation of a theory-based model is what gives power to the sense-making approach described previously.

Recommendation 2.6

Develop a supporting science for visual analytics, integrating research in analytical reasoning and sense-making as well as the principles of perception and cognition that underlie interactive visualization.

This science must be built on integrated perceptual and cognitive theories that embrace the dynamic interaction among cognition, perception, and action. It must provide insight on fundamental cognitive concepts such as attention and memory. It must build basic knowledge about the psychological foundations of concepts such as *meaning, flow, confidence,* and *abstraction.*

To be effective, the science of visual analytics must be developed within the context of the demands of visual analytics systems. This research will be different from and much more than task analysis. It will be an integration of basic research with a specific task domain to create robust and practical results that advance both visual analytics and efforts to understand the fundamental workings of the human mind.

The goal of a supporting science for visual analytics is large, but research must focus on particular components of the visual analytics domain to meet the homeland security challenge. Key components are analytic reasoning (discussed in this chapter) and interactive visualization (discussed in Chapter 3).

To achieve this objective, we must develop a supporting science for the analytical reasoning process itself. Heuer [1999] contributes an important summary of the aspects of perception, memory, and cognitive biases that affect analysis. He focuses on the fundamental limits that constrain the process of analysis and provides analytical methods for compensating for these limits. However, a fully developed science must include constructive theories and models as well as such guidelines.

With the ever-increasing complexity of the challenge, it is important to better understand abstraction and how people create, evaluate, and compare such "mental models" to first make sense and then take action based on these models. Understanding abstraction clearly supports not only the design of tools to create (or help users create) abstractions but also the ability to capture the reasoning process and its artifacts.

In visual analytics, the process of analytical reasoning, or deriving meaning from masses of data, is supported by interactive visualization. "Using pictures to think" is a primary component of visual analytics, but analysis is a process that must involve action, and thus interaction, at all its stages. Thus, the supporting science for visual analytics must also include the development of theories and principles for how interactive visualization works both perceptually and cognitively to support analytical reasoning. An integrated model of visualization, especially visualization as mediated by interaction, could be used in a constructive and evaluative form on a broad range of visualization tasks and data.

Recommendation 2.7

Research how visual analytic systems function at the micro levels of perception and cognition, especially in focusing user attention and facilitating cognitive shifts.

There is a great need to study visual analytic systems at the micro level. In visual analytic systems, visual form is given to conceptual abstractions. While in some cases automated reasoning techniques may be used within analytical tools as an aid to the analyst, in many cases visual analytics tools instead use well-chosen data representations and transformations that help the analyst to recognize and discover information. The success of an analytical tool can be strongly affected by low-level visual attention phenomena.

A detailed-level understanding of how visualizations work at the perceptual and cognitive level does not exist yet. This understanding is an important foundation that must be established to support the construction of visual analytics systems. We must better understand how to capture and focus attention and how to facilitate cognitive shifts, especially to avoid missing alternative hypotheses and solutions. An accurate model of attention would have a profound impact on analysis, but it would also have relevance to other issues ranging from the effectiveness of multimodal interfaces to general support for multi-tasking.

Collaborative Visual Analytics

As the scenarios in Chapter 1 illustrate, homeland security challenges are so complex and dynamic that they cannot be addressed by individuals working in isolation. Threat analysis, border protection, and emergency management and response efforts are of sufficiently large scale and importance that they must be addressed through the coordinated action of multiple groups of people, often with different backgrounds and working in disparate locations with differing information. Here, the issue of human scalability plays a critical role, as systems must support the communications needs of these groups of people working together across space and time, in high-stress and time-sensitive environments, to make critical decisions.

According to the *Intelligence Community Collaboration Baseline Study Report* [Hall, 1999], "Collaboration is broadly defined as the interaction among two or more individuals and can encompass a variety of behaviors, including communication, information sharing, coordination, cooperation, problem solving, and negotiation."

In relation to knowledge management in the context of intelligence, Waltz [2003] lists the following functions for collaboration:

- Coordinate tasking and workflow to meet shared goals.
- Share information, beliefs, and concepts.
- Perform cooperative problem-solving analysis and synthesis.
- Perform cooperative decision making.
- Author team reports of decisions and rationale.

Advances in collaborative visual analytics have the potential to enable each of these functions for teams of individuals as well as for organizations; they are central to the problem-solving analysis and synthesis function. Enabling joint work requires support for both *cooperative-competitive* dialogue (in which team members or different teams work toward the same goals but pose competitive explanations and solutions) and *collaborative* dialogue (in which team members share a problem conceptualization, share responsibilities, and coordinate). Both types of dialogue are typically needed within the same analytical reasoning task, as analysts cycle between focused attention and controlled broadening components of the analytic discourse and sense-making processes described earlier in this chapter.

In an emergency, collaboration among agencies and with the first responder communities is essential. Agencies, including neighboring state and local governments, collaborate to share available resources. They must maintain a clear shared understanding of the capabilities and status of available resources, whether they are fire trucks or hospital beds. In an emergency, decisions must be made quickly using the best available information. The role of visual analytics is to assist in sharing information with the best available minds so that informed decisions can be made. Information must be shared with experts to answer difficult and previously unanticipated questions, such as how to protect the public in the event of a chemical explosion.

State of the Art

Collaborative situations can be categorized with respect to space and time as shown in Figure 2.6 [Waltz, 2003]. This time and space matrix distinguishes between support of local and distributed (space) working contexts and between synchronous or asynchronous (time) work situations [Johansen, 1988]. There has been extensive research in Computer Supported Collaborative Work (CSCW) and other communities in all four quadrants of this diagram. However, attention to the role of visualization in cooperative work and to the process of cooperative-competitive (or collaborative) analytical reasoning has been limited. Below, we briefly highlight key aspects of the current state of the art and identify critical gaps in both knowledge and analytic methods relevant to development and application of collaborative visual analytics.

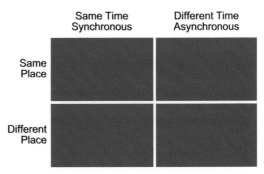

Figure 2.6. Typology of collaborative situations.

Supporting same place, synchronous work

Same place, synchronous work involves groups of people meeting face to face. This has been extensively studied, both to improve the productivity of group interactions and to define a baseline for the other quadrants of collaborative situations. It is clear that people working together use speech, gesture, gaze, and nonverbal cues to attempt to communicate in the clearest possible fashion. In addition, real objects and interactions with the real world can also play an important role in face-to-face collaboration. Garfinkel [1967, 1970], Schegloff and Sacks [1973], and Mehan and Wood [1975] all report that people use the resources of the real world to establish shared understanding. In addition, Suchman [1988] reports that writing and drawing activities could be used to display understanding and facilitate turn taking in much the same way that other non-verbal conversational cues do. In collaborative teamwork, team members coordinate their actions around the artifacts and the spaces they occupy [Hollan, 1992].

To advance collaborative visual analytics, it is essential to understand and support group reasoning with a range of analytic reasoning artifacts. McNeese and colleagues [2000a, 2000b] have investigated the use of *perceptual anchors*, or externalized representations that map to mental models, in individual and team problem solving related to search and rescue. They have identified interactions between individual and team problem-solving strategies and studied the transfer of successful strategies to other problem contexts. They are working toward collaborative tools that alleviate problem-solving weaknesses for both individual and group problem solving.

Although technology can be used to enhance face-to-face collaboration, it can also negatively affect the communication cues transmitted between collaborators. The effect of mediating technology can be better understood through the use of communication models, such as Clark and Brennan's theory of "grounding" [1991]. In this case, conversational participants attempt to reach shared understanding using the available communication channels modified by the available technology. Olson and Olson [2001] provide a list of 10 key characteristics of face-to-face interaction that can be used as a guide for comparing the effect of technologies on collaboration.

Visually based analysis tools encourage problem solving and brainstorming in team environments, but research is required in order to take full advantage of the power that these tools can provide in a team setting.

Supporting different place, synchronous work

Another class of collaborative technologies supports distributed, synchronous work. The most common example is distributed meetings. Synchronized audio and shared presentations are now commonly used in business meetings. For example, NetMeeting, Placeware, and WebEx are applications that allow several participants to teleconference while simultaneously viewing a slide presentation or sharing a computer demonstration. Shared chat rooms are another example of a popular CSCW application. These applications are beginning to have a large impact on business practices.

Emergency response situations clearly demand support for distributed teams of people working together synchronously. Communication must take place among the responders in the field, the emergency operations centers involved, and the incident commander, who is the decision maker in the field. Information must be shared to the level necessary to support decision making, and information must be preserved to illustrate why decisions were made. This history becomes extremely important if an emergency grows in size and jurisdiction so that additional agencies become involved and control for the overall emergency response transfers from one organization to another.

Two-way communication must be supported. Responders in the field provide real-time sharing of information about what is happening at the scene, while operations centers provide direction and response. Communication in the field is primarily through tools such as cell phones and web-based applications for information sharing. Although the emphasis is on portable communication, these devices are vulnerable to disruptions in connectivity.

Each emergency is unique, so the team's focus must be on applying their training and experience to the new situation. The tools used to support emergency response must take into account the highly stressful nature of the situation. Tools must be extremely simple and clear to use, because user attention must be focused on the emergency rather than the mechanics of the software.

Visual analytic methods can be extended (or invented) to support distributed synchronous work such as emergency response. The challenges include:

- Developing effective interfaces to visual displays and visual analytics tools operating on multiple kinds and sizes of devices in varied circumstances (for example, mobile devices used in field operations)
- Supporting analysis of continually updating geospatially referenced information of heterogeneous form (for example, map-based field annotations, streaming video, photos and remote imagery, sensor networks)
- Supporting coordinated reasoning and command-control through the complex, multi-scale organizational structures of emergency response.

In general, CSCW research suggests that a remote communications space should have three elements: high-quality audio communication, visual representations of the users, and an underlying spatial model. These elements correspond to the three available communication channels: audio, visual, and environmental. The affordances of the communications technology used will modulate the cues carried by each of these channels [Gaver, 1992]. The unique stress and urgency of many analysis and emergency response situations may pose special demands on the remote, real-time collaborations. Research is needed to determine whether the general rules of thumb in typical collaborative situations hold true in high-pressure analysis and emergency response situations as well.

To understand the effect of technology on remote collaboration, many experiments have been conducted comparing face-to-face, audio-and-video, and audio-only communication. Not unexpectedly, when visual cues are removed, the communication behavior changes; however, performance in an audio-only condition may be unchanged. Even with no video delay, video-mediated conversation doesn't produce the same conversational style as face-to-face interaction. These results suggest that technology may not be able to replace the experience of shared presence and that research should focus on ways to provide experiences that go "beyond being there" [Hollan, 1992]. Examples include a tool that allows a remote expert to look through the eyes of a novice and place virtual annotations in his or her environment to improve performance on a real-world task [Bauer et al., 1999] or a tool that allows the novice to access a context-sensitive, expert-derived template for application of a visual analytic method.

Supporting different place, asynchronous work

In a distributed organization, work takes place at different places and at different times. In emergency preparedness activities, for example, distributed and asynchronous collaboration is feasible and valuable. Longer-term analytical efforts can also be supported through distributed and asynchronous collaboration.

Sharing information across place and time is one of the main reasons the internet is so popular. But the internet has spawned many technologies besides dynamic, linked documents. *Wikis* are collaborative documents that anyone may edit. They incorporate version control and simple editing and formatting protocols such as structured text so that a group of people can easily and safely edit a collection of web pages. Wikis are commonly used to organize complex projects. Web logs, or blogs, and remote syndication services, or RSS, are other examples of online technology that are rapidly spreading. Blogs provide simple interfaces for maintaining online diaries. RSS notifies interested parties when new content is available. Web-based collaboration technologies are among the fastest growing internet applications.

Over the past decade, scientific attention and resources have been directed to development of scientific collaboratories. This work can be leveraged to develop methods and tools that support collaborative visual analytics. The concept of national collaboratories to enable science was articulated in a 1993 National Research Council report [Cerf et al., 1993]. This report characterizes a collaboratory as a "... center without walls, in which the nation's researchers can perform research without regard to geographical location—interacting with colleagues, accessing instrumentation, sharing data and computational resources, and accessing information from digital libraries." Considerable progress has been made toward the report goals (e.g., Kouzes et al. [1996], Olson et al. [2001]), particularly for collaboratories that facilitate research in physical or medical sciences and on real-time data collection or control of experiments.

These efforts have shown that there are several requirements for supporting remote asynchronous work [Maher & Rutherford, 1997; Dufner et al., 1994], including:

- Support for a shared workspace, enabling easy distribution and access of data
- Access to an application domain with all the shared applications needed
- A data management system, ensuring data consistency and concurrency control
- Access to a reference area with links to relevant online material
- Tools/support structures for asynchronous messaging and communication
- A focus on data-centric (rather than connection-centric) collaboration
- Tools for recording collaboration history and data changes
- Security and privacy control.

Supporting same place, asynchronous work

Co-located, asynchronous collaboration is focused on place-based communication among members of an analytic or command and control team. Continuous operations in emergency operations centers represent a good example of co-located asynchronous communication. Individuals from an earlier work shift must preserve relevant information and decisions made for their colleagues who are working succeeding shifts. Although there is some overlapping time during the shift change process so that important information can be transferred in person, much of the communication still takes place asynchronously.

Collaborative work in this category often centers on large shared displays, or collections of such displays, sometimes called *interactive workspaces* [Johansen, 1988; Streitz et al., 1999]. The displays are used in such environments to replace flipcharts and whiteboards, as well as large computer screens visible to collaborative teams [Pedersen et al., 1993; Abowd et al., 1998]. By extending these technologies, the work process may be captured and annotated, making it possible to capture histories of collaborative analysis.

One example is the MERBoard, which has a large, shared display used as the portal into a repository of shared information and which can be accessed by different users at different times. MERBoard was designed at the Jet Propulsion Laboratory (JPL) in collaboration with International Business Machines Corporation (IBM) to support the planning, decision making, and execution of the Mars Exploration Rovers. Personnel at the National Aeronautics and Space Administration (NASA) use a large, interactive display to share and access mission data. Remote users can view and interact with the display using a shared desktop protocol such as Virtual Network Computing (VNC). The MERBoard is an outgrowth of the IBM BlueBoard, which was originally designed for walk-up meetings and collaborations. However, current research on this system is focused on interactive, shared visualizations, such as the status of IBM's 200+ servers, presented in a form easily accessible by systems administration staff. An overview of both systems is provided in Russell et al. [2004]. Unlike traditional command and control centers, systems such as MERBoard and BlueBoard are designed for easy, walk-up use.

The role of visual display for cooperative/competitive analytical reasoning

Dynamic visual analytics environments have at least three distinct roles in support of cooperative/competitive analytical reasoning:

1. As a representation of the features in the world that are the object of focus, thus as a model of the physical world (e.g., maps depict aspects of the world critical to situation assessment and planning of actions associated with emergency management) and as a mechanism to assemble a view into an information space populated by an array of information artifacts

2. As a support for analytic discourse among collaborators as they reason (individually, cooperatively, and competitively) about strategies for information analysis, situation assessment (and the strength of evidence that underlies the assessment), hypotheses about future developments, and plans for action

3. As a support for coordinated activity (e.g., helping to synchronize the actions of multiple participants in that activity). See MacEachren [1995].

Considerable attention has been directed to the role of external (usually visual) representations in enabling collaboration generally. This attention, however, is fragmented, appearing in a range of disciplines from CSCW through diagrammatic reasoning and argument visualization [Johansen, 1988], to multimodal interfaces for geospatial information [McGee et al., 2001]. For example, Suthers has implemented concepts from diagrammatic reasoning in an open-source toolkit for collaborative learning (http://sourceforge.net/projects/belvedere/) and has conducted several empirical studies of the impact of abstract visual representations on reasoning and hypothesis generation. In one study, Suthers et al. [2003] found that visually structured representations (graph, matrix) influenced representation and discussion of evidential relations, with a matrix increasing discussion but graphs producing more focused consideration of evidence. Complementary to these efforts to understand the role of particular kinds of visual representation on collaboration, progress has been made in understanding the general role of external (usually visual) representations and artifacts in the cognitive process of groups [Zhang, 2001].

Sharing information and perspective

In an effort to describe features of the world and manage associated knowledge, domains that range from computational sciences and artificial intelligence (e.g., Gaver [1992]) to the environmental and social sciences (e.g., Fonesca et al. [2002]) have developed knowledge representation languages and constructed ontologies that use them. This prior work, however, is missing a key element that is critical to supporting collaborative visual analytics in the intelligence analysis and emergency management domains: consideration of how knowledge is generated, revised, promulgated, shared, built upon, and retired. Formal representation of knowledge typically focuses on recording propositions and rules about a domain without attempting to situate knowledge in the context of its creation or use. As discussed for sense-making above, knowledge representation and management to support collaborative visual analytics requires that knowledge is situated in the context of its creation, use, sharing, and re-use.

Many have described human-computer interaction as a conversation or dialogue—with oneself, with one's current collaborators, with future actors, with a machine [Nake & Grabowski, 2001; Winograd & Flores, 1986; MacEachren, 2004]. We propose extending the notion of human-information dialogue, or analytic discourse, as the vehicle to help analysts uncover the lineage and basis of shared ideas as they move from one analyst to another, from one information source to another, from one geographic context to another, and from one time to another. This approach complements recent efforts in visualization of argumentation to support science work [Shum et al., 2003].

Supporting distributed cognition/common ground

In his study of shipboard navigation on Navy vessels, Edwin Hutchins [1996] illustrated that critical insights about coordinated team activity can be achieved by applying a distributed cognition perspective. From this perspective, teamwork is viewed as a process in which aspects of cognition are distributed across the collaborating agents, which in this case are individuals with different roles and tasks, and the artifacts through which the agents acquire, construct, and share knowledge. A distributed cognition perspective has been adopted as a framework for understanding group work in contexts that include complex team problem solving in shared information spaces, the development of team situation awareness for emergency operations and military action, and the process of collaborative urban design.

A successful distributed cognition process, whether distributed among individuals and artifacts that are co-located or geographically distributed, requires that participants establish common ground through a set of shared pertinent knowledge, beliefs, and assumptions [Klein et al., 2004]. Chuah & Roth [2003] contend that visualization tools can be used to help collaborators establish common ground and have developed an environment within their Command Post of the Future project for creating collaborative information analysis and decision-making applications. Common ground in this system is established through a combination of explicitly shared objects and events, representations of level of attention directed to objects, depiction of goals for analyzing objects and events, representation of interpretations and thoughts through annotations and sketches, and representation of object history.

Theory, Knowledge, and Technology Needs

Current visual analytic methods and tools are designed for use by individuals. However, the homeland security challenges facing the nation require concerted, cooperative, and coordinated efforts by teams and sets of teams that bring a range of expertise to the task. Our goals range from developing fundamental knowledge about the role of visual analytics in enabling team cognition to advancing the technology to facilitate coordinated, distributed analytical reasoning. Key goals include the following:

- Develop a better understanding of how interactive visualization is used for coordination, for collaborative analysis together across space and time, and for establishing and managing group dynamics.
- Take advantage of knowledge of perception and cognition and advances in display technology to apply the new display technology productively to support co-located and distributed work teams.
- Learn from, apply, and extend developments in collaborative visualization, group games and simulation models, and multi-criteria decision-support systems.
- Develop strategies for connecting visualization and semantic frameworks that underpin analytic discourse.
- Understand how the analytic sense-making, reasoning, and judgment process differs for teams—and develop methods and tools to meet the needs of teams and to enable analytic reasoning outcomes that are more than the sum of the parts, thus generating key insights through juxtaposition and/or integration of perspectives.
- Understand and support the role of team-enabled visual analytics in each stage of the sense-making processes in threat analysis and emergency response.
- Apply knowledge from addressing the above goals to developing visual analytics systems that enable analytic discourse and coordinated action within teams.

These goals lead to the following recommendation.

Recommendation 2.8

Develop a theory and approaches to characterize and enhance the ways visual analytics is used for coordination and collaboration, especially in situations of high stress and great urgency; more specifically, discover how analytic processes can be enabled by interactive visualization so that distributed expertise is better exploited and clear communication is enabled.

Visual analytics methods and tools must support the work of analyst/decision-maker teams, ranging from small work groups applying collective expertise to relatively narrow analytic problems to cross-organizational, distributed teams faced with complex information sifting and analysis tasks. In emergency situations, where information is ambiguous and collaboration is taking place with a wide range of people under extreme time pressure and at great consequence, collaboration is paramount.

Visual analytics tools must also support seamless interaction with information of heterogeneous forms, derived from heterogeneous sources, and having varied ontological structures. A key goal is to develop methods that support capture, encoding, and sharing of both explicit and tacit knowledge derived from integrated exploration of diverse sources and that support use of encoded knowledge from these diverse sources to generate and mediate among alternative interpretations of evidence and plans for action.

Summary

The goal of visual analytics is to facilitate the analytical reasoning process through the creation of software that maximizes human capacity to perceive, understand, and reason about complex and dynamic data and situations. It builds upon an understanding of the reasoning process, as well as an understanding of underlying cognitive and perceptual principles, to provide mission-appropriate interactions that allow analysts to have a true discourse with their information. This discourse is essential to facilitating informed judgment with a limited investment of the analysts' time.

Summary Recommendations

The following high-level recommendations summarize the detailed recommendations from this chapter. These actions are necessary to advance the science of analytical reasoning in support of visual analytics.

Recommendation:

Build upon theoretical foundations of reasoning, sense-making, cognition, and perception to create visually enabled tools to support collaborative analytic reasoning about complex and dynamic problems.

To support the analytical reasoning process, we must enable the analyst to focus on what is truly important. We must support the processes involved in making sense of information and developing and evaluating alternative explanations. Tools and techniques must support both convergent thinking and divergent thinking. These tools and techniques also must allow analysts to look at their problem at multiple levels of abstraction and support reasoning about situations that change over time, sometimes very rapidly. They must support collaboration and teamwork, often among people with very different backgrounds and levels of expertise. Accomplishing this will require the development of theory to describe how interactive visual discourse works, both perceptually and cognitively, in support of analytical reasoning.

Recommendation:

Conduct research to address the challenges and seize the opportunities posed by the scale of the analytic problem. The issues of scale are manifested in many ways, including the complexity and urgency of the analytical task, the massive volume of diverse and dynamic data involved in the analysis, and challenges of collaborating among groups of people involved in the analysis, prevention, and response efforts.

The sheer volume and scale of data involved in the analytical process offer as many opportunities as they do challenges for visual analytics. A science of scalable, visually based analytical reasoning, or visual analytic discourse, must take the issue of scale into consideration. Different types of analytic discourse will be appropriate to different analytical tasks, based on the level of complexity of the task, the speed with which a conclusion must be reached, the data volumes and types, and the level of collaboration involved.

References

Abowd G, J Brotherton, and J Bhalodia. 1998. "Classroom 2000: A System for Capturing and Accessing Multimedia Classroom Experiences." In *Proceedings of CHI 98: Human Factors in Computing Systems*, pp. 20-21. Association for Computing Machinery, Los Angeles.

Adams JL. 2001. *Conceptual Blockbusting: A Guide to Better Ideas*. Fourth edition, Perseus Publishing, Cambridge, Massachusetts.

Bauer M, G Kortuem, and Z Segall. 1999. "Where Are You Pointing At? A Study of Remote Collaboration in a Wearable Videoconference System." In *Proceedings of the 3rd International Symposium on Wearable Computers*, pp. 151-158, San Francisco.

Bertin J. 1981. *Graphics and Graphic Information Processing*. Walter De Gruyter, Inc., Berlin.

Bodnar JW. 2003. *Warning Analysis for the Information Age: Rethinking the Intelligence Process*. Joint Military Intelligence College, Center for Strategic Intelligence Research, Washington, D.C.

Boyd JR. 1987. *A Discourse on Winning and Losing*. Document No. MU 43947, Air University Library, Maxwell Air Force Base, Alabama.

Bush V. July 1945. "As We May Think." *Atlantic Monthly* 176:101-108.

Card SK, JD Mackinlay, and B Shneiderman. 1999. *Readings in Information Visualization: Using Vision to Think*. Morgan Kaufmann Publishers, San Francisco.

Card SK, GG Robertson, and JD Mackinley. 1991. "The Information Visualizer: An Information Workspace." In *Proceedings of the ACM Conference on Human Factors in Computing Systems* (CHI '91), pp. 181-186, ACM Press, New York.

Central Intelligence Agency (CIA). 1995. *P1000 Strategic Plan for Information Visualization*. CIA/AIPASG (Advanced Information Processing and Analysis Steering Group)/AR&DC (Advanced Research and Development Committee). Washington, D.C.

Central Intelligence Agency (CIA). 1997. "CIA Opens the Door on the Craft of Analysis." *Center for Study of Intelligence Newsletter*. No. 5, Winter-Spring 1997. Washington, D.C.

Cerf VG, AGW Cameron, J Lederberg, CT Russell, BR Schatz, PMB Shames, LS Sproull, RA Weller, and WA Wulf. 1993. *National Collaboratories: Applying Information Technology for Scientific Research*. National Academies Press, Washington, D.C.

Chen C. 2003. *Mapping Scientific Frontiers: The Quest for Knowledge Visualization*. Springer-Verlag, London.

Chuah MC and SF Roth. 2003. "Visualizing Common Ground." In *Proceedings of the Seventh International Conference on Information Visualization*, pp. 365-372, July 16-18, 2003.

Clark HH and S Brennan. 1991. "Grounding in Communication." In *Perspectives on Socially Shared Cognition*, eds. LB Resnick, J Levine, and SD Teasley. APA Press, Washington, D.C.

Descartes R. 1637. *Discourse on Method*.

Dufner DK, SR Hiltz, and M Turoff. 1994. "Distributed Group Support: A Preliminary Analysis of the Effects of the Use of Voting Tools and Sequential Procedures." In *Proceedings of the 27th Annual Hawaii International Conference on System Sciences (HICSS)*, Vol. III, pp.114-123.

Endsley MR. 1995. "Situation Awareness and the Cognitive Management of Complex Systems." *Human Factors Special Issue* 37(1):85-104.

Fonseca F, M Egenhofer, P Agouris, and G Câmara. 2002. "Using Ontologies for Integrated Geographic Information Systems." *Transactions in GIS* 6(3):231-257.

Garfinkel H. 1967. *Studies in Ethnomethodology*. Prentice-Hall, Englewood Cliffs, New Jersey.

Garfinkel H and H Sacks. 1970. "On Formal Structures of Practical Action." In *Theoretical Sociology: Perspectives and Developments*, eds. JC McKinney and EA Tiryakian, Appleton-Century-Crofts, New York.

Gaver W. 1992. "The Affordances of Media Spaces for Collaboration." In *Proceedings of the 1992 Conference on Computer Supported Cooperative*, Toronto, Canada, pp. 17-24, Oct. 31-Nov. 4, 1992, ACM Press, New York.

Gibson JJ. 1986. *The Ecological Approach to Visual Perception*. Lawrence Erlbaum Associates, Hillsdale, New Jersey.

Hall T. 1999. CIA's *Baseline Study for Intelligence Community Collaboration: Final Report*. Information Sharing Solutions Office of Advanced Analytic Tools, Central Intelligence Agency. Available at http://collaboration.mitre.org/prail/IC_Collaboration_Baseline_Study_Final_Report/toc.htm.

Heuer R. 1999. *Psychology of Intelligence Analysis*. U.S. Government Printing Office, Washington, D.C.

Hollan J and S Stornetta. 1992. "Beyond Being There." In *Proceedings of CHI '92*, pp.119-125, ACM Press, New York.

Hutchins E. 1996. *Cognition in the Wild*. MIT Press, Cambridge, Massachusetts.

Johansen R. 1988. *Groupware: Computer Support for Business Teams*. Free Press, New York.

Jones M. 1995. *The Thinker's Toolkit: 14 Powerful Techniques for Problem Solving*. Three Rivers Press, New York.

Jones S and M Scaife. 2000. "Animated Diagrams: An Investigation into the Cognitive Effects of Using Animation to Illustrate Dynamic Processes." In *Theory and Application of Diagrams, Lecture Notes in Artificial Intelligence*, No. 1889:231-244. Springer-Verlag, Berlin.

Kirschner PA, SJB Shum, and CS Carr. 2003. *Visualizing Argumentation: Software Tools for Collaborative and Educational Sense-Making*. Springer-Verlag, London.

Klahr D. 2000. *Exploring Science: The Cognition and Development of Discovery Processes*. Bradford Books, Cambridge, Massachusetts.

Klein G, PJ Feltovich, JM Bradshaw, and DD Woods. In Press. "Common Ground and Coordination in Joint Activity." In *Organization Simulation*, eds. WB Rouse and KR Boff. John Wiley & Sons, New York.

Klein G, JK Phillips, EL Rall, and DA Peluso. In Press. "A Data/Frame Theory of Sense-Making." In *Expertise Out of Context*, ed. R Hoffman. Lawrence Erlbaum Associates, Mahwah, New Jersey.

Klein GA. 1989. "Recognition-Primed Decisions." In *Advances in Man-Machine Systems Research*, ed. WB Rouse, JAI Press, Inc., Greenwich, Connecticut.

Klein GA. 1998. *Sources of Power: How People Make Decisions*. MIT Press, Cambridge, Massachusetts.

Kouzes RT, JD Myers, and WA Wulf. 1996. "Collaboratories: Doing Science on the Internet." *IEEE Computer* 29(8):40-46.

Larkin J and HA Simon. 1987. "Why a Diagram Is (Sometimes) Worth Ten Thousand Words." *Cognitive Science* 11:65-99.

Lederberg J. 1989. "Preface: Twelve-Step Process for Scientific Experiments: Epicycles of Scientific Discovery." *Excitement and Fascination of Science*. Annual Reviews, Inc., Palo Alto, California.

Leedom DK. 2001. *Final Report: Sense-Making Symposium*. (Technical Report prepared under contract for Office of Assistant Secretary of Defense for Command, Control.) Evidence-Based Research, Inc., Vienna, Virginia.

MacEachren AM. 1995. *How Maps Work: Representation, Visualization, and Design*. The Guilford Press, New York.

MacEachren AM. In Press. "Moving Geovisualization Toward Support for Group Work." In *Exploring Geovisualization*, eds. J Dykes, AM MacEachren, and MJ Kraak. Elsevier, Oxford.

MacEachren AM and I Brewer. 2004. "Developing a Conceptual Framework for Visually-Enabled Geocollaboration." *International Journal of Geographical Information Science* 18(1):1-34.

MacEachren AM and MJ Kraak. 2001. "Research Challenges in Geovisualization." *Cartography and Geographic Information Science* 28(1):3-12.

MacEachren AM, M Gahegan, and W Pike. 2004. "Visualization for Constructing and Sharing Geoscientific Concepts." In *Proceedings of the National Academy of Science*, 101(suppl. 1):5279-5286.

Maher ML and JH Rutherford. 1997. "A Model for Synchronous Collaborative Design Using CAD and Database Management." *Research in Engineering Design* 9:85-98.

McGee DR, M Pavel, and PR Cohen. 2001. "Context Shifts: Extending the Meaning of Physical Objects with Language." *Human-Computer Interaction* 16:351-362.

McNeese MD and MA Vidulich, eds. 2002. *Cognitive Systems Engineering in Military Aviation Environments: Avoiding Cogminutia Fragmentosa!* Human Systems Analysis Center, Wright-Patterson Air Force Base, Ohio.

McNeese MD, K Perusich, and JR Rentsch. 2000. "Advancing Socio-Technical Systems Design via the Living Laboratory." In *Proceedings of the Industrial Ergonomics Association/Human Factors and Ergonomics Society (IEA/HFES) 2000 Congress*, pp. 2-610-2-613.

McNeese MD, E Theodorou, L Ferzandi, T Jefferson, and X Ge. 2000. "Distributed Cognition in Shared Information, Spaces." In *Proceedings of the 46th Annual Meeting of the Human Factors and Ergonomics Society*, pp. 556-560.

Mehan H and H Wood. 1975. *The Reality of Ethnomethodology*. John Wiley & Sons, New York.

Nake F and S Grabowski. 2001. "Human-Computer Interaction Viewed as Pseudo-Communication." *Knowledge-Based Systems* 14:441-447. National Research Council. 2003. *IT Roadmap to a Geospatial Future*. National Academies Press,Washington, D.C.

Norman DA. 1993. *Things That Make Us Smart*. Addison-Wesley, Reading, Massachusetts.

Olson JS and GM Olson. 2000. "i2i Trust in E-Commerce." *Communications of the ACM* 43(12):41-44.

Olson GM, TW Malone, and JB Smith. 2001. *Coordination Theory and Collaboration Technology*. Lawrence Erlbaum Associates, Mahwah, New Jersey.

Patel VL, JF Arocha, and DR Kaufman. 1994. "Diagnostic Reasoning and Medical Expertise." *The Psychology of Learning and Motivation* 31:187-252.

Patel V, G Groen, and Y Patel. 1997. "Cognitive Aspects of Clinical Performance During Patient Workup: The Role of Medical Expertise." *Advances in Health Sciences Education* 2:95-114.

Patterson ES, EM Roth, and DD Woods. 2001. "Predicting Vulnerabilities in Computer-Supported Inferential Analysis Under Data Overload." *Cognition, Technology & Work* 3:224-237.

Pedersen, ER, K McCall, TP Moran, and FG Halasz. 1993. "Tivoli: An Electronic Whiteboard for Informal Workgroup Meetings." In *Proceedings of the SIGCHI Conference on Human Factors in Computing Systems*, pp. 391-398, ACM Press, New York.

Pirolli P and SK Card. 1999. "Information Foraging." *Psychological Review* 106(4):643-675.

Pirolli P and S Card. 2005. "Sensemaking Processes of Intelligence Analysts and Possible Leverage Points as Identified Through Cognitive Task Analysis" (6 pp.). In *Proceedings of the 2005 International Conference on Intelligence Analysis*, McLean, Virginia.

Pylyshyn Z. 2003. *Seeing and Visualizing: It's Not What You Think*. MIT Press, Cambridge, Massachusetts.

Resnikoff HL. 1989. *The Illusion of Reality*. Springer-Verlag, New York.

Rheingans P. 1992. "Color, Change, and Control for Quantitative Data Display." In *Proceedings of the 3rd Conference on Visualization '92*, October 19-23, Boston, pp. 252-259.

Russell DM, MJ Stefik, P Pirolli, and SK Card. 1993. "The Cost Structure of Sense-making." In *Proceedings of the SIGCHI Conference on Human Factors in Computing Systems*, pp. 269-276. Amsterdam. ACM Press, New York.

Russell DM, JP Trimble, and A Dieberger. 2004. "The Use Patterns of Large, Interactive Display Surfaces: Case Studies of Media Design and Use for BlueBoard and MERBoard." In *Proceedings of the 37th Hawaii International Conference on System Sciences*, pp. 98-107, IEEE Computer Society Press, Los Alamitos, California.

Sanders AF. 1984. "Ten Symposia on Attention and Performance: Some Issues and Trends." *Attention and Performance X*. Lawrence Erlbaum Associates, London.

Schegloff E and H Sacks. 1973. "Opening up Closings." *Semiotica* 8:289-327.

Schum DA. 1994. *The Evidential Foundations of Probabilistic Reasoning*. Northwestern University Reasoning Press, Evanston, Illinois.

Shrager J and P Langley. 1990. *Computational Models of Scientific Discovery and Theory Formation*. Morgan Kaufmann, San Francisco.

Shum SB, V Uren, G Li, J Domingue, and E Motta. 2003. "Visualizing Internetworked Argumentation." Chapter 9 in *Visualizing Argumentation: Software Tools for Collaborative and Educational Sense-Making*, eds. PA Kirschner, SJB Shum, and CS Carr, Springer-Verlag, London.

Simon HA. 1996. *The Sciences of the Artificial*. Third edition, MIT Press, Cambridge, Massachusetts.

Small HG and B Griffith. 1974. "The Structure of Scientific Literatures. 1. Identifying and Graphing Specialties." *Science Studies* 4:17-40.

Spohrer JC and DC Engelbart. 2004. "Converging Technologies for Enhancing Human Performance: Science and Business Perspectives." *Annals of the New York Academy of Sciences* 1013:50-82.

Streitz NA, J Geißler, T Holmer, S Konomi, C Müller-Tomfelde, W Reischl, P Rexroth P Seitz, and R Steinmetz. 1999. "i-LAND: An Interactive Landscape for Creativity and Innovation." In *Proceedings of the SIGCHI Conference on Human Factors in Computing Systems: The CHI Is the Limit*, pp. 120-127, Pittsburgh, Pennsylvania, May 15-20, 1999. ACM Press, New York.

Suchman L. 1988. "Representing Practice in Cognitive Science." *Human Studies* 11:305-325.

Suthers D and C Hundhausen. 2003. "An Experimental Study of the Effects of Representational Guidance on Collaborative Learning." *Journal of the Learning Sciences* 12(2):183-219.

Suthers D, L Girardeau, and C Hundhausen. 2003. "Deictic Roles of External Representations in Face-to-Face and Online Collaboration: Designing for Change in Networked Learning Environments." In *Proceedings of the International Conference on Computer Support for Collaborative Learning*, pp. 173-182.

Taylor RM, MC Bonner, B Dickson, H Howells, CA Miller, N Milton, K Pleydell-Pearce, N Shadbolt, J Tennison, and S Whitecross. 2001. "Cognitive Cockpit Engineering: Coupling Functional State Assessment, Task Knowledge Management, and Decision Support for Context-Sensitive Aiding." *Human Systems IAC Gateway Newsletter* XII(1):20-21. Human Systems Analysis Center, Wright-Patterson Air Force Base, Ohio.

Tenet GJ. 1999. *Consumer's Guide to Intelligence*. Diane Publishing Company, Collingdale, Pennsylvania.

Tufte ER. 1983. *The Visual Display of Quantitative Information*. Graphics Press, Cheshire, Connecticut.

Varela FJ, E Thompson, and E Rosch. 1991. *The Embodied Mind: Cognitive Science and Human Experience*. MIT Press, Cambridge, Massachusetts.

Waltz E. 2003. *Knowledge Management in the Intelligence Enterprise*. Artech House, Boston.

Ware C. 2004. *Information Visualization: Perception for Design*. Second edition, Morgan Kaufmann, San Francisco.

Weick KE. 1995. *Sense-Making in Organizations*. Sage Publications, Thousand Oaks, California.

Wickens C and J Hollands. 2000. *Engineering Psychology and Human Performance*. Third edition, Prentice Hall, Upper Saddle River, New Jersey.

Winograd T and F Flores. 1986. *Understanding Computers and Cognition*. Ablex, Norwood, New Jersey.

Woods DD, ES Patterson, EM Roth, and K Christofferson. 2002. "Can We Ever Escape from Data Overload?" *Cognition, Technology & Work* 4:22-36.

Zhang J. 1997. "Distributed Representation as a Principle for the Analysis of Cockpit Information Displays." *International Journal of Aviation Psychology* 7(2):105-121.

Zhang J. 2001. "External Representations in Complex Information Processing Tasks." A Kent, ed., in *Encyclopedia of Library and Information Science*. Marcel Dekker, Inc., New York.

"Discovery consists of seeing what everybody has seen and thinking what nobody has thought."

—Albert von Szent-Gyorgyi (1893–1986)

3

Visual Representations and Interaction Technologies

The use of visual representations and interactions to accelerate rapid insight into complex data is what distinguishes visual analytics software from other types of analytical tools. Visual representations translate data into a visible form that highlights important features, including commonalities and anomalies. These visual representations make it easy for users to perceive salient aspects of their data quickly. Augmenting the cognitive reasoning process with perceptual reasoning through visual representations permits the analytical reasoning process to become faster and more focused.

It is a challenge to create well-constructed visual representations. In the field of scientific visualization, data often correspond to real-world objects and phenomena, meaning that there are natural visual representations. In scientific visualization, the goal is to mimic these real-world representations as faithfully as computationally feasible. However, most visual analytics problems deal with abstract information so the researcher is left to select the best representation for the information.

Visual representations invite the user to explore his or her data. This exploration requires that the user be able to interact with the data to understand trends and anomalies, isolate and reorganize information as appropriate, and engage in the analytical reasoning process described in Chapter 2. It is through these interactions that the analyst achieves insight.

This chapter discusses important aspects of visual representations and interaction techniques necessary to support visual analytics. It covers five primary topics. First, it addresses the need for scientific principles for depicting information. Next, it focuses on methods for interacting with visualizations and considers the opportunities available given recent developments in input and display technologies. Third, it addresses the research and technology needed to develop new visual paradigms that support analytical reasoning. Then, it discusses the impact of scale issues on the creation of effective visual representations and interactions. Finally, it considers alternative ways to construct visualization systems more efficiently.

Visual analytics tools can support people working under great time pressure, whether they are analysts, emergency management and response staff, or border personnel. Well-crafted visual representations can play a critical role in making information clear. The visual representations and interactions we develop must readily support users of varying backgrounds and expertise. In an emergency situation, for example, personnel may need to use unfamiliar systems to gain the insight that they need to respond. Visual representations and interactions must be developed with the full range of users in mind, from the experienced user to the novice working under intense time pressure, so that visual analytics tools can achieve their promise.

Developing Principles for Depicting Information

The design of visual representations of information has been ongoing for centuries. Over the past 20 years, driven by the ever-increasing speed and availability of computers, information visualization researchers have invented dynamic and interactive computer-mediated visual metaphors for representing abstract information. A new discipline is rapidly emerging around the creation of computer-mediated visual representations to support display and analysis of information.

Some of these new techniques work well and have generated great excitement. However, the number of successful new computer-mediated visual representations today is small compared to the number of highly evolved and widely used metaphors created by human information designers. Human-designed visualizations are still much better than those created by our information visualization systems.

State of the Art

The creation of computer-mediated visual representations has much in common with other emerging disciplines. An emerging discipline progresses through four stages. It starts as a craft and is practiced by skilled artisans using heuristic methods. Later, researchers formulate scientific principles and theories to gain insights about the processes. Eventually, engineers refine these principles and insights to determine production rules. Finally, the technology becomes widely available. The challenge is to move from craft to science to engineering to systems that can be widely deployed.

Today, we are still in the early stages of development of the discipline. We lack fundamental understanding of the basic principles for effectively conveying information using graphical techniques. Without fundamental knowledge of what makes certain representations effective, it is not possible to efficiently construct new representations for new classes of information or to know that the new representations will work as designed. Poorly designed visualizations may lead to an incorrect decision and great harm. (A famous example is the poor visualizations of the O-ring data produced before the disastrous launch of the Challenger space shuttle, as discussed more fully in Tufte [1997] and Chapter 5.) Thus, we need to develop scientific principles for effectively conveying information.

Cognitive scientists have studied visual representations and the larger class of *external aids to cognition*. An external aid to cognition is an artifact that helps us reason about the world. In the physical world, we build and use power tools to extend our physical abilities. In the same way, in the world of information, we build cognitive tools to extend our reasoning abilities. Visual representations are the equivalent of power tools for analytical reasoning.

A first step in developing principles for visual representations is to understand how they enable cognition [Card, 1999; Norman, 1993]. Some basic principles for developing effective depictions include the following (adapted from [Norman, 1993]):

- **Appropriateness Principle** – The visual representation should provide neither more nor less information than that needed for the task at hand. Additional information may be distracting and makes the task more difficult.
- **Naturalness Principle** – Experiential cognition is most effective when the properties of the visual representation most closely match the information being represented. This principle supports the idea that new visual metaphors are only useful for representing information when they match the user's cognitive model of the information. Purely artificial visual metaphors can actually hinder understanding.
- **Matching Principle** – Representations of information are most effective when they match the task to be performed by the user. Effective visual representations should present affordances suggestive of the appropriate action.

Another prominent cognitive scientist has suggested the following two basic principles [Tversky et al., 2002]:

- **Principle of Congruence** – The structure and content of a visualization should correspond to the structure and content of the desired mental representation. In other words, the visual representation should represent the important concepts in the domain of interest.
- **Principle of Apprehension** - The structure and content of a visualization should be readily and accurately perceived and comprehended.

The subjects of mental representations and reasoning are the main focus of cognitive science, so the principles for depicting information must be based on research in cognitive science. The apprehension principle underlies the importance of research in perception. These meta-principles underscore that the biggest challenge in choosing a visual representation is to find the *right* one (not just any one) for the reasoning task at hand.

The next step to take in developing a set of design principles is to formally define the different types of visualizations. The French cartographer Bertin has developed a system for characterizing representations of charts, maps, and networks [Bertin, 1981]. Bertin considered the space of possible visual representations as a visual language. The spatial and visual attributes of the image encode the information using the rules of the language. Bertin's system has since been used to define a design space of information visualizations. Examples of extensions are Mackinlay [1986], Roth et al. [1991], MacEachren [1995], Card et al. [1999], and Stolte [2002]. Wilkinson [1999] has developed an extensive grammar for graphics. Others have tried to develop taxonomies of visual techniques [Shneiderman, 1996; Spence, 2000; Ware, 2000]. The most notable is Shneiderman's taxonomy, which breaks down visualization by the characteristics of the data (1D, 2D, nD, network, etc.). Although these design spaces and taxonomies are very promising, we are far from having a complete, formally developed theory of visual representations.

After defining the space of visualizations, Bertin developed design principles for choosing among the possibilities. He argued that the properties of the visual representation should match the properties of the data representation. For example, color represents nominal data well because hue is not naturally ordered. Although Bertin provides a set of principles loosely based on perception, it is important to realize that his system is not based on rigorous experiments involving human subjects. Bertin also did not emphasize the importance of the task when choosing a visual representation.

Another notable attempt to provide design principles for statistical graphics is the work of Cleveland [1985]. Some of Cleveland's recommendations are based on experiments in graphical perception [Cleveland & McGill, 1984]. Perceptual design principles have also been developed for color [Rogowitz & Treinish, 1993] and motion [Bartram & Ware, 2002]. However, scientific principles are rare, and most recommendations are based on general principles of graphic design. Tufte's three outstanding books on information presentation [1983, 1990, 1997] also stress the importance of using principles regularly practiced by graphic designers. Best practices have also been developed for different domains such as statistical graphics [Cleveland, 1985] and cartography [MacEachren, 1995]. Tukey [1977] was also a strong advocate of using graphics in data analysis and developed many visual representations that are now common in statistics. To move the field of visual analytics forward, we need to perform more research in developing scientifically tested design principles.

Recent work in the information visualization community has attempted to systematically apply design principles to the automatic generation of visualizations. Mackinlay [1986] developed Automated Presentation Tool (APT) that automatically designed charts based on Bertin's and Cleveland's ideas. APT searches over a space of possible visual representations, evaluates them based on expressiveness and effectiveness criteria, and chooses the best one. This work has been extended by Roth and colleagues [Roth, 1991; Zhou, 1999]. There has also been recent work on using cognitive design principles for automatically producing route maps [Agrawala et al., 2003] and assembly instructions [Heiser et al., 2004]. In the future, most visualizations will be generated by machines as users interact with the information, so automating the presentation of information will become increasingly important.

Technology Needs

The systems described here are only initial steps toward solving the major problems in creating a complete set of cognitive, perceptual, and graphic design principles. The creation of analysis systems that are based on cognitive, perceptual, and graphic design principles will dramatically improve the efficiency, effectiveness, and capabilities of analysts, decision makers, scientists, and engineers.

Recommendation 3.1

Conduct research to formally define the design spaces that capture different classes of visualizations.

We must both characterize the taxonomy of visual representations that must be considered and describe the range of design parameters associated with these representations. While there is a body of work available to draw upon, as described above, this work has not been targeted specifically at visual representations in support of analysis. We must build upon and extend this work to create a formal definition of the range of available visual representations.

Recommendation 3.2

Develop a set of scientifically based cognitive, perceptual, and graphic design principles for mapping information to visual representations.

Using the taxonomy created above, we must define the set of principles for selecting the most promising visual representations to support a specific combination of analytic task and data characteristics. These principles must be verified through user testing. In addition, we must develop and test principles for selection of the specific visualization properties to support specific tasks and data characteristics.

The use of design patterns has become an accepted and useful technique in areas such as object-oriented design and software engineering [Gamma, 1994]. We must investigate whether we can develop a set of visual design patterns for both designing new visualizations and determining the types of visualizations most useful for particular analytic tasks. One potential approach is to develop a library of common visualization design patterns from which developers could draw to build new visualizations.

A Science of Interaction

Visual analytics is not simply about presenting information. Rather, an analysis session is more of a dialogue between the analyst and the data, where the visual representation is simply the interface or view into the data. In an analysis dialogue, the analyst observes the current data representation, interprets and makes sense of what he or she sees, and then thinks of the next question to ask, essentially formulating a strategy for how to proceed [Card et al., 1999; Spence, 2000]. Undoubtedly, new questions occur to the analyst and new factors must be considered. Thus, a different perspective on the data will be needed and new variables will need to be considered. The manifestation of this dialogue is the analyst's interactions with the data representation. How does the analyst request other perspectives on the data? How does the analyst filter out unwanted details? How does the analyst request new visual representations of the data?

State of the Art

Too often in the visual analytic process, researchers tend to focus on visual representations of the data but interaction design is not given equal priority. We need to develop a "science of interaction" rooted in a deep understanding of the different forms of interaction and their respective benefits. The mantra by Shneiderman

[1996] of "*Overview first, zoom and filter, details on demand*" is well-accepted, but what are the next steps, or additional different steps?

There are at least three ways to look at the science of interaction. First, we can look at interaction from the point of view of human time constants. This is an important viewpoint because all interaction is constrained and driven by what the user is cognitively and perceptually capable of doing. Second, we can look at how interaction is used to accomplish tasks such as data manipulation, manipulation of visual mappings, navigation, and dialogue. Third, we can look at the nature of the interaction itself, including the differences between interactions in 2-dimensional (2D) and 3-dimensional (3D) environments and the effects of the devices used for interaction. Each of these viewpoints yields different insights into the current state of the art, as described below.

Levels of interaction: human time constants

Analysis of human time constants for human-computer interaction was initially discussed by Card et al. [1983], considered from a cognitive science point of view by Newell [1990], and discussed from an information visualization point of view by Card et al. [1999]. Newell describes four bands of time scales for human action (biological, cognitive, rational, and social) ranging from 100 microseconds to months. For purposes of a science of interaction for analytical reasoning, the two bands of greatest focus are Newell's cognitive (100 milliseconds to 10 seconds) and rational (minutes to hours) bands. Card describes three distinct bands within Newell's cognitive band. Note that these time constants represent approximate time ranges. That is, when we say ~100 milliseconds, we mean somewhere in the range of 50 to 300 milliseconds.

~100 milliseconds. Card refers to this as the *perceptual fusion time constant*, while Newell refers to it as the *deliberate act time constant*. This time constant is the rate necessary to produce the perception of a smooth animation. In animation, 10 frames per second equates to 100 milliseconds per frame. In interaction design, this time constant is the rate necessary to create the perception of an immediate response. Users expect to see an immediate response when they move a dynamic query slider [Ahlberg, 1994]. Likewise, as users brush over items of interest, they expect to see immediate corresponding highlighting of the linked items [Cleveland, 1999]. This time constant is also important because minimum human motor response time is around 250 milliseconds.

~1 second. Card refers to this as the *unprepared response time*, while Newell refers to it as the *operation time*. For our purposes, this constant represents the necessary rate of response to simple user actions. For example, clicking a web link should produce the display of the next web page within 1 second to be effective. If the response might take more time, it is important to provide some kind of feedback in the 1-second timeframe to reassure the user that something is happening. This time constant is also important for interactive animation, like user-initiated transition animations (transitions from one complex structure to another or one viewpoint to another). It has been demonstrated that providing a 1-second transition animation can reduce user task performance time compared to providing no transition animation [Robertson et al., 2002].

~10 seconds. Both Card and Newell refer to this as the *unit task time*. This is the time within which users expect more complex user-initiated activities to complete (e.g., a complex search). Again, if an activity of this kind will take more than 10 seconds to complete, it is important to provide the user with feedback within this 10-second timeframe.

~100 seconds (minutes to hours). This is referred to as the *rational band*. Higher-level reasoning processes, including the analytic reasoning and human-information discourse processes described in Chapter 2, take place in this band. Interaction techniques in this timeframe rely heavily on complex cognitive processing and are greatly affected by attentional resource demands such as interruptions and shifts in focus. These techniques are the least well understood and developed.

Uses of interaction

Card et al. [1999] identify three primary uses of interaction for information visualization: to modify data transformation (filtering), to modify visual mappings, and to modify view transformation (i.e., navigation). For visual analytics, we add a fourth use, which is for human-information discourse, a higher-level user dialogue with the information.

Interactions for modifying data transformation (filtering). Several common techniques are in use today, including direct manipulation, dynamic queries [Ahlberg, 1994], brushing [Cleveland & McGill, 1984], and details-on-demand.

Interactions for modifying visual mappings. Dataflow systems [Haeberli, 1988] and Pivot Tables are two examples of techniques that allow the user to interactively change mappings between the data and their visual representations.

Interactions for modifying view transformation (navigation). Interaction techniques range from simple approaches like direct selection for selecting and highlighting objects of interest, to more complex camera control techniques in 3D environments. They also include techniques for panning and zooming [Bederson et al., 1996] as well as for achieving a balance between overview and detail [Plaisant et al., 1995].

Interaction for human-information discourse. The least well understood use of interaction is to support a true human-information discourse in which the mechanics of interaction vanish into a seamless flow of problem solving. Interactions are needed to support processes such as comparing and categorizing data, extracting and recombining data, creating and testing hypotheses, and annotating data.

To date, there has been no foundational work to characterize the design space of these interaction techniques. We really do not know if the techniques that have been created thus far are the best or most appropriate techniques.

Nature of interactions

The nature of an interaction is affected by whether it takes place in a 2D or 3D environment. The best developed interaction techniques have been for 2D visualizations and 2D graphical user interfaces. While a lot of work has been devoted to interaction techniques for 3D virtual environments, they are not nearly as well developed as the 2D techniques. 3D manipulation and navigation techniques tend to be harder to use and harder to learn. One promising approach for simplifying interaction in 3D environments has been to identify cases where 3D visual representations are used, but the interactions are constrained so that 2D interaction techniques can be used. An example of this is the Data Mountain [Robertson et al., 1998], where a 3D visual representation is used but object manipulation takes place on a tilted plane.

Interaction can also be greatly affected by the display and interaction devices used for visual analytics tasks. A wide range of display configurations will be used to support visual analytics; hence, interaction techniques should be designed so that they are similar across different devices ranging from large shared displays to desktop environments to field-portable devices. While this is technically challenging to do, it has been done in at least one case. DateLens [Bederson et al., 2004] is a scalable calendar system that works on everything from a personal digital assistant (PDA) display to a wall-sized display, scaling the visual representation to the appropriate size for the device and using the same interaction technique at all scales.

While most interaction techniques use a single modality (or human sense), there is work that suggests that multimodal interfaces can overcome problems that any one modality may have. For example, voice and deictic (e.g., pointing) gestures can complement each other and make it easier for the user to accomplish certain tasks [Oviatt, 1999]. Sonification can be used to enhance visualization either by redundant encoding of visual information in the auditory channel [Robertson, 1998] or by use of sound to represent data values [Smith et al., 1990].

Technology Needs

Although a lot of isolated design work has been done in specific aspects of interaction science, little systematic examination of the design space has been done. As a field, we are in a transition phase in which researchers are beginning the foundational work to understand that design space. Creating a science of interaction is critical because the large-scale nature of the analytic problem and the compressed timeframe for analysis require that we identify and develop the correct interaction techniques for any given human timeframe, interaction use, or interaction environment.

Basic interaction techniques

To achieve successful adoption, visual analytics software must support both basic interactions and highly sophisticated interactions that support the analytic reasoning process. Before these more sophisticated interactions can be addressed systematically, work is needed to create a scientific understanding about the basic interactions that are used to support simpler operations. This understanding will form the foundation for research into more sophisticated interactions.

Recommendation 3.3

Create a new science of interaction to support visual analytics.

The grand challenge of interaction is to develop a taxonomy to describe the design space of interaction techniques that supports the science of analytical reasoning. We must characterize this design space and identify under-explored areas that are relevant to visual analytics. Then, R&D should be focused on expanding the repertoire of interaction techniques that can fill those gaps in the design space.

Interaction techniques for human-information discourse

Existing work on interaction techniques for human-computer interaction and information visualization has focused on cognitive time bands, interaction for data manipulation, visual mapping manipulation, and navigation. The discussion on analytic discourse and sense-making in Chapter 2 makes it clear the higher-level dialogue between analyst and information, or human-information discourse, is of vital importance. This discourse involves the rational time band and higher-level uses of interaction, but neither has been sufficiently explored.

Recommendation 3.4

Expand the science of interaction to support the human-information discourse needed for analytical reasoning. In particular, identify and develop interaction techniques that support higher-level reasoning and that address the rational human timeframe.

Human beings are very skilled at analyzing complex situations using a combination of their available information and their combined knowledge and experience. However, there are inherent human tendencies that analysts must recognize and overcome. Interaction techniques must be developed that support an analytic discourse and help compensate for human limitations, including:

- **Information overload in complex situations**. Techniques are needed to help analysts simplify their cognitive load without compromising the analyst's effectiveness and to help compensate for faulty memory.
- **Overcoming biases**. Biases affect the way data are interpreted. Biases about the reliability of different sources may lead people to discount information from sources that aren't considered reliable. People often see what they expect to see and tend to ignore evidence that is contradictory to a preferred theory. If they form a preliminary judgment too early in the analytical process, they may hold firm to it long after the evidence invalidates it [Heuer, 1999].
- **Satisficing**. People settle for a "good enough" answer, sometimes stopping their analytical process before they identify critical information that would lead them to a different conclusion [Heuer, 1999].

New interaction techniques are needed to support the user in evaluating evidence, challenging assumptions, and finding alternatives. Analytical environments should support the user in identifying and understanding all relevant information to reach a solid conclusion rapidly. The tools we create need to establish a correct balance between structure and intuition.

Leveraging New Media to Support Interaction

While it is not expected that the visual analytics research community will need to focus on inventing new display technologies, the ability to harness the power of new display and interaction technologies invented by others will be one key to success. Advances in the past decade have led to new discoveries in terms of the capacity and manner in which visualizations can be displayed and interacted with. Traditional desktop displays, which appeared stuck for several years with Cathode Ray Tube (CRT) technology at resolutions below a mega-pixel, are now rapidly changing in terms of resolution and form factor. As these and even more dramatic changes occur, it will be important for visual analytic researchers to remain abreast of these changes and to use new techniques for expressing data with the new media.

Harnessing new display technologies

On the desktop, a variety of technologies exist to enable display and interaction with visualizations. These range from the traditional single-mega-pixel CRT computer monitors to 3D Liquid Crystal Displays (LCDs) to multi-mega-pixel LCDs.

While stereovision has been available on the desktop for many years, displays that free the user from goggles are recent introductions to the marketplace and potentially will have a greater penetration and therefore more availability to users of visual analytics. As these displays merge with traditional 2D displays and the prices normalize, an opportunity exists for researchers to use this technology in their applications.

While stereo on the desktop has been available for years, this technology is still relatively unexplored. However, users quickly adopt improvements in screen resolution and size. Multi-mega-pixel displays are offered by most monitor vendors and are being rapidly adopted at both homes and offices. Improvements in LCD technologies are providing displays of up to 60 inches while resolutions have approached nearly 10 mega-pixels (although not at such extreme display sizes). Other technologies like Liquid Crystal on Silicon (LCOS) are expected to take such improvements to LCDs to the next level. These improvements are only expected to increase and should be considered by those developing visual analytic techniques.

Form factor and resolution are only a few of the expected improvements in the coming years to display technologies. We believe that new technologies like the Organic Light-Emitting Diode (OLED) displays will improve viewing angle, weigh less, and be more cost effective, brighter, and power efficient [Tang & Van Slyke, 1987].

Recommendation 3.5

Develop visual representations and interaction techniques that exploit new display devices for visual analytics.

Mobile technologies will play a role in visual analytics, especially to users that are on the front line of homeland security. First responders now use technologies like cell phones and PDAs; in the future, they will use new technologies like foldable displays, electronic inks, or virtual retinal displays [Wang et al., 1999; Kollin, 1993]. These technologies, which allow flexible, lightweight, and wearable options for users, will allow information to rapidly be disseminated to users in field. Researchers must devise new methods to best employ these technologies and provide a means to allow data to scale between high-resolution displays in command and control centers to field-deployable displays.

Scaling to multiple devices and device configurations

To support homeland security missions, visual analytics applications must support applications ranging from an operations center using shared large-screen displays or potentially augmented reality displays, to the individual analyst working at a desktop computer to first responders and border personnel using handheld, field-portable devices. Users need to have a consistent set of interactions that they can count on regardless of the device they are using. This is especially true in emergency situations, when users' attention is directed toward the immediate situation and mechanics of the computer system must be second nature to the user.

Develop interaction techniques that scale across different devices and are used in the same way on platforms ranging from handheld, field-portable devices to wall-sized displays.

Many common desktop computing interaction methods are not currently portable to other devices. Research is needed to develop interaction techniques that both optimize the opportunities offered by new devices and provide consistency of operation across devices.

For large and multiple displays, there is a benefit to seeing more information for more people and to enabling interactive group collaboration. Furthermore, increased screen real estate enables new research efforts into peripheral awareness of information [Greenberg & Rounding, 2001; Cadiz et al., 2002; Stasko, 2004]. Extra displays could be used to help analysts stay aware of information and might facilitate "noticing" important facts. The availability of added display space may foster the development of new information representations, ones that simply were not practical on traditional, single-monitor systems. Multiple or distributed display environments, however, present a whole new set of challenges for interaction and navigation. Navigating with a mouse over a large display area can become slow and tiresome, for example. Thus, new interaction techniques for these environments are needed [Baudisch et al., 2003; Hutchings, 2004; Robertson et al., 2004].

Multimodal interaction

Voice and gesture complement each other and, when used together, can create an interface more powerful than either modality alone. Oviatt [1999] shows how natural language interaction is suited for descriptive techniques, while gestural interaction is ideal for direct manipulation of objects. Unlike gestural or mouse input, voice is not tied to a spatial metaphor. Voice can interact with objects regardless of degree of visual exposure, particularly valuable in a graphical environment where objects may be hidden inside each other or occluded by other objects.

Users prefer using combined voice and gestural communication over either modality alone when attempting graphics manipulation. Hauptman and MacAvinney [1993] used a simulated speech and gesture recognizer in an experiment to judge the range of vocabulary and gestures used in a typical graphics task. Three different modes were tested: gesture only, voice only, and gesture and voice recognition. Users overwhelmingly preferred combined voice and gestural recognition because of the greater expressiveness possible. Users were also able to express commands with greatest sufficiency using combined input.

Some tasks are inherently graphical; others are verbal; and yet others require both vocal and gestural input to be completed. Allowing both types of input maximizes the usefulness of the environment by broadening the range of tasks that can be done intuitively. Also, allowing both types of input would enable analysts to vocally annotate how discoveries were made and replay sequences to others.

There are also psychological reasons for integrating speech and gesture recognition into a virtual environment. Experiments in cognitive psychology have shown that a person's ability to perform multiple tasks is affected by whether these tasks use the same or different sensory modes, for example visuo-spatial or verbal modes. According to the multiple resource theory of attention [Kinsbourne & Hicks, 1978; Wickens, 1980], the brain modularizes the processing of different types of information—when different tasks tap different resources, much of the processing can go on in parallel. Such is the case with speech and visuo-spatial modalities. Thus, by adding speech input to the visual environment, users should be able to perform visuo-spatial tasks at the same time as giving verbal commands with less cognitive interference.

Experimental evidence supports this theory. Investigating attentional capacity, Treisman and Davis [1973] found that the ability to concentrate on more than one task at a time was expanded when the tasks were presented in separate perceptual channels and people responded to them across different response channels. This is in part due to the spatial and verbal information being stored separately in human memory [Baddeley & Hitch, 1974]. Martin [1989] finds that the benefits of multiple modalities previously demonstrated with separate, multiple tasks also extend to single-task, multiple-component situations more typical of human-computer interactions.

The level to which multimodal interfaces can bring benefit to the analytical reasoning process has yet to be fully explored, however.

Recommendation 3.7

Investigate the applicability of multimodal interaction techniques for visual analytics.

The combination of gestural and voice interaction has produced some promising research results, but it has not been widely adopted in application. Visual analytics supports much more complex reasoning tasks than have been the subject of previous research on multimodal interfaces. Additional study is needed to see how multimodal interfaces affect the effectiveness and efficiency of the analytical process. We should investigate the use of multimodal interfaces for both individual analysts and collaborative teams of analysts. In addition, research is needed to determine the value of multimodal interfaces in field conditions faced by border personnel and by distributed teams working in noisy and time-sensitive emergency situations.

New Visual Paradigms to Support Analytic Reasoning

Over the last 20 years, numerous new visual representations, interaction methods, software tools, and systems have been developed. Often these representations and tools have been developed without considering the analytical reasoning tasks that they support. Meaningful visualization techniques for complex information must be task-driven.

In this section we consider various reasoning tasks of critical importance and outline the types of visual representations that need to be developed.

Organizing Large Collections of Information

Today, two primary ways to organize information spaces exist: the graphical desktop user interface and information displayed by search engines. The desktop interface consists of hierarchically organized folders containing documents. It was designed in an era when floppy disks were common and file systems contained thousands of documents. A desktop interface to handle larger collections of information is badly needed. Search engines developed by companies such as Google™, Inktomi®, Yahoo!®, and Microsoft® Corporation organize large interconnected document collections. The interfaces are query-driven and show only small result sets. No information is given about the space of all documents. Search technology is now being deployed to help organize the desktop, e-mail, and other information spaces.

Information visualization systems, such as IN-SPIRE™, allow thousands of documents to be visually, succinctly described, navigated, and accessed. The ThemeView™ 3D visual landscape shown in Figure 3.1 reflects the high-dimensional properties and relationships of sets of documents by showing clusters of themes and their strengths. The complex content is visible. Exploration, summarization, comparison, trends over time, tracking, and many other operations are more efficient. The strengths of visualization and document vector mathematics are combined to achieve a new analytical capability for massive data [Hetzler & Turner, 2004].

SeeSoft [Eick et al., 1992] provides a visual representation of all source code in a large software system, as shown in Figure 3.2. The system represents lines of code from software files in successively smaller fonts, ultimately representing the most deeply indented lines as individual rows of pixels whose indentation and line length tracks the original text. The color of each row encodes an attribute such as the age, author, or function of the corresponding line of code. This representation captures the sequential nature of source code, shows critical loops in the code, and allows overlays of additional information. SeeSoft shows the information inside each source code file, as well as relationships across the files. For example, the lines of code written by a single developer can be shown both within a file and across multiple files.

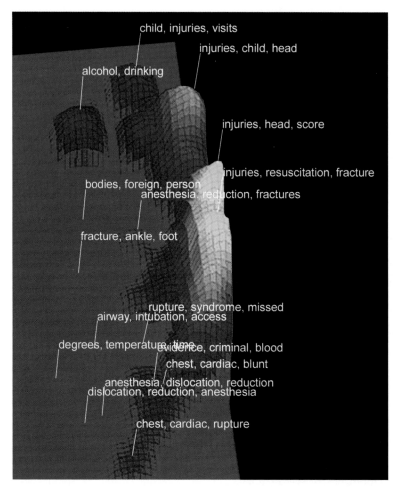

Figure 3.1. *The IN-SPIRE software's ThemeView landscape shows relationships among documents. High peaks represent prominent themes. Peaks close together represent clusters of similar documents.*

Figure 3.2 shows an entire module from this software system with color showing age of each line. The reduced representation provides an overview, shows the new code, old code, and frequently changed code. This example highlights how an effective representation of a domain, such as software in this example, becomes a critical visual tool to enable understanding of the structure of the code and patterns of maintenance in the code that were not possible before it was created.

Another example of a set of integrated views of an information space is the Command Post of the Future system described in Chapter 5. Used in military applications, it presents a comprehensive map-based view of the operational area. The map provides a unified information space that is populated with intelligence assessments and planned activities.

Figure 3.2. *Left: SeeSoft representation for software source code where successively smaller fonts lead to a "reduced" single row of pixels per line of source code. Right: Module in a software system with color encoding the age of lines of code.*

These examples illustrate the value of showing large integrated views of dynamic information spaces. However, much more work is needed to support the full range of analytic tasks faced by the analyst and accommodate the demands of analyzing massive and complex data collections.

Recommendation 3.8

Create visual analytic tools that provide integrated views of large-scale information spaces, support coordinated viewing of information in context, and provide overview and detail.

Integrated views of data can support and improve perception and evaluation of complex situations by not forcing the analyst to perceptually and cognitively integrate multiple separate elements. Visualization systems should present all the relevant information required for a decision maker or operator to efficiently and correctly comprehend and act in a complex situation. Systems that force a user to view sequence after sequence of information are time-consuming and error-prone [Kapler & Wright, 2004; Mooshage et al., 2002].

Similarly, combining or merging interactions and controls with visible representations can also speed access, control, and manipulation operations. Often, users experience a cognitive separation between the task they want to accomplish and the mechanics for accomplishing the task. New techniques can be invented that do away with the separation of "what I want and the act of doing it" [Van Dam, 2001]. Integrating views, interactions, and analytics provides significant productivity improvement for the combined human, analytical, and data system.

To provide the maximum information for the user, visual representations are routinely combined with textual labels. The generation of meaningful labels and their placement on the display represents an often-overlooked challenge. Labels should be visible without overwhelming the display or confusing users. The number of labels, their placement, and their content are all areas for further investigation.

Cartographers have long wrestled with this problem and their work offers valuable lessons, but interactive systems and dynamic data bring new challenges and opportunities to labeling.

Analysts working with large data sets want to gain a global understanding of the data and then focus on particular data items and their attributes. Alternating among levels of detail generates moment-to-moment insights and spurs new questions. A number of visualization and user interface techniques have been developed to support coordinated views of both overview and detail. Greene et al. [2000] found that previews and overviews help users quickly understand the scope of their data set and discriminate between interesting and uninteresting content. Existing techniques include the use of multiple coordinated windows at different focus levels, panning and zooming operations, and so-called "fisheye" views [Plaisant et al., 1995; Furnas, 1986]. Fisheye techniques are "focus+context" views, i.e., one in which both the overview and detail are presented side by side in the same view. The power of "focus+context" comes from the ability to subjugate unimportant information for contextual navigation while using attentive focus for effectively communicating information. While existing techniques in this area are very useful, new methods must be developed that take advantage of multiple and large-area computer displays to assist analysts with inquiries on the massive data sets evident in visual analytics.

Reasoning about Space and Time

Because of our daily need to navigate and reason about the world around us, people are particularly good at reasoning about space and time. Maps, which are one of the earliest visual inventions of the human race, abstract the space around us in ways that support various forms of reasoning. Modern geographic information systems provide access to large amounts of geospatial information, including satellite imagery, digital terrain models, and detailed maps of roads and cities. To support analysis, this information must be studied in a temporal context.

Cartographers have developed representations such as flow maps [Dent, 1999] that show migration patterns on top of maps. The common weather map is an example of a flow map. Understanding how best to combine time and space in visual representations needs further study. For example, in the flow map, spatial information is primary (i.e., it defines the coordinate system of the visualization). Why is this the case, and are there visual representations where time is foregrounded that could also be used to support analytical tasks?

An example of an innovative system is GeoTime™, shown in Figure 3.3. Geo-Time works with the spatial inter-connectedness of information over time and geography within a single, highly interactive 3D view. Events are represented within an X,Y,T coordinate space. Patterns of activity among people, places, and activities can be analyzed. Connectivity analytical functions help find groups of related objects [Kapler & Wright, 2004].

While systems such as GeoTime show great promise, the challenge of integrated spatial and temporal reasoning is still a substantial one.

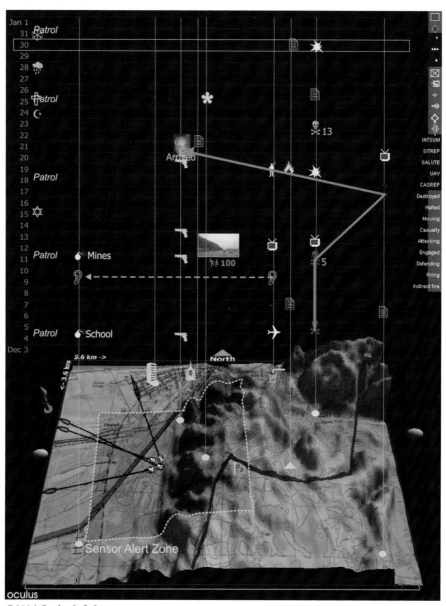

©2004 Oculus Info Inc.

Figure 3.3. *GeoTime provides an integrated view for analysis of a combination of temporal and geospatial data.*

Develop tools that leverage humans' innate abilities to reason about space and time.

Analyzing observations over time and geography typically requires multiple, separate tools, e.g., a map for geospatial information and a timeline for the temporal information. Representations of time that support temporal reasoning are less studied and less developed than representations of geospatial data. Navigation and other problems that involve reasoning about space are well studied; however, reasoning about sequence of events is not as well understood.

Not only must we deepen the research understanding about temporal reasoning, but we must create task-appropriate methods for integrating spatial and temporal dimensions of data into visual representations.

Abstraction – Changing to the Appropriate Representation

To show what is important and why it is important is exceedingly difficult. Illustrators have successfully developed a powerful set of principles for concisely conveying complex information in an appropriate way. The objective is "to create an abstraction that conveys key ideas while suppressing irrelevant detail." The challenge is to be able to assess a situation, extract key features, and visually represent those features and their combinations effectively. This needs to be done dynamically as conditions, interests, and tasks change [Foley, 2000; Smallman et al., 2001].

There are two interrelated issues in dealing with abstraction. The first is the development of an analytic capability to transform data from one representation to another. Selecting relevant information, filtering out unneeded information, performing calculations, sorting, and clustering are all components of data abstraction. Second is the development of techniques for visual abstraction. Visual abstraction involves developing effective representations for different types of information. Visual abstraction also involves the control of emphasis and level of detail. Different representations of the same object may be needed at different levels of detail, depending on the importance of that object for the given task. Secondary visual attributes can also be used to connote additional attributes that are important in reasoning, such as the quality of the data or the confidence in the assessment.

One particular challenge is to develop automatic, user-driven techniques for changing representation. The Pad++ system uses a zoomable interface to navigate a document collection. As the user zooms into a folder or document, more detail is shown. The system changes representations based on the *semantics* of the data, and hence it is possible to do meaningful *semantic zooms*. Other examples of multi-scale interfaces include Woodruff [1998] and Stolte et al. [2002].

Rendering techniques that support cognitive abstraction from visual representations and improve understanding of complex information spaces must also be incorporated into visual analytic solutions. These techniques include advanced rendering methods that aid 3D perception (e.g., advanced illumination, shading, texturing, transparency, shadowing) as well as illustrative rendering techniques that support design and illustration principles (e.g., effective design [Agrawala et al., 2003; Heiser et al., 2004], volume illustration [Rheingans & Ebert, 2002; Svakhine et al., 2003; Treveat & Chen, 2000]).

Recommendation 3.10

Develop visual representation methods for complex information that provide the appropriate level of abstraction.

Research is necessary to:

- Identify alternative visual representations of data that best support different analytical tasks
- Develop transformation methods that allow the user to move among alternative visual representations to facilitate exploration and discovery
- Provide level of emphasis and detail appropriate to the user's data and task.

Uncertainty – Understanding Incomplete or Erroneous Information

Reasoning and working with uncertain information is common in most visual analytics applications. To reach the appropriate conclusions, analysts must remain fully aware of the uncertainties and conflicts present in their information. However, representation of uncertainty is not often considered in current visual analytics systems.

Recommendation 3.11

Develop visual representations that illustrate uncertain, missing, and misleading information, and that allow the analyst to understand the uncertainty inherent in visual analytics applications.

There is no accepted methodology to represent potentially erroneous information, such as varying precision, error, conflicting evidence, or incomplete information. There is no agreement on factors regarding the nature of uncertainty, quality of source, and relevance to a particular decision or assessment. Nevertheless, interactive visualization methods are needed that allow users to see what is missing, what is known, what is unknown, and what is conjectured, so that they may infer possible alternative explanations. Uncertainty must be displayed if it is to be reasoned with and incorporated into the visual analytics process. In existing visualizations, much of the information is displayed as if it were "true" [Finger & Bisantz, 2002].

Integrating Powerful Analysis Tools with Visualization

Data representation and transformation (described more fully in Chapter 4) evolved from the statistics, pattern recognition, and machine-learning communities and have long been a staple in analysis. These approaches are powerful, automated, and quantitative.

Unfortunately, data transformation approaches, by themselves, are insufficient to provide the required insights. Visual analytics couples these computational capabilities with a human decision maker. The hybrid system is more powerful than either the machine or the analyst working alone.

Many possible data transformations may be applicable to a particular problem, but it is not necessarily clear which ones will be of most value in facilitating insight. Visual analytics offers advantages to the user because it provides visual cues that can help the analyst formulate a set of viable models. Also, because visual analytics is qualitative as well as quantitative, there are no assumptions of exact parameters and well-defined boundaries between what is interesting and what is not. A priori criteria of significance may be manipulated based on the judgment of the analyst. The weaknesses of visual analytics are that there are often infinite possibilities in terms of mappings and views, and there is a high potential for information overload in dense information fields.

Many analytic packages support multiple visual representations and computational techniques, although generally each will emphasize one over the other. For example, plots are routinely used to confirm analysis and sampling, and clustering algorithms are often used for data reduction prior to visual exploration. The problem is that the communication between the two forms of analysis is often a thin, one-directional channel.

Recommendation 3.12

Develop visual analytic methods that combine data transformations with interactive visual tools, leveraging powerful computational methods that are developed for continuous and discrete data analysis with human cognitive and perceptual abilities.

An ideal environment for analysis would have a seamless integration of computational and visual techniques. For instance, the visual overview may be based on some preliminary data transformations appropriate to the data and task. Interactive focusing, selecting, and filtering could be used to isolate data associated with a hypothesis, which could then be passed to an analysis engine with informed parameter settings. Results could be superimposed on the original information to show the difference between the raw data and the computed model, with errors highlighted visually. This process could be iterated if the resulting model did not match the data with sufficient accuracy, or the analyst could refocus on a different subspace of information.

An environment that strongly links data transformation and visualization will result in more powerful analysis process that allows the user to draw on the strengths of each approach.

Monitoring Streams of Data – Assessing Situations and Detecting Changes

Many analytic activities involve monitoring a stream of information. The analyst is required to identify and respond to major new developments. We need a new visualization paradigm that will enable analysts to extract relevant information from information streams, gain situational awareness, and formulate appropriate actions.

Streaming data are particularly important for homeland security applications. With the decreasing cost of silicon, it has become cost-effective to deploy new sensor systems that are capable of collecting massive information streams. The systems will collect much more data than can be combined and warehoused in a centralized system. Thus we need to develop fundamentally new techniques to visualize and analyze data in motion.

As an example, we consider an ongoing project at University of Illinois-Chicago National Center for Data Mining. In this project, shown in Figure 3.4, traffic data from the tri-state region (Illinois, Indiana, and Wisconsin) are collected from hundreds of embedded sensors. The sensors are able to identify vehicle weights and traffic volumes. There are also cameras that capture live video feeds, Global Positioning System (GPS) information from selected vehicles, textual accident reports, and weather information. The research challenge is to integrate this massive information

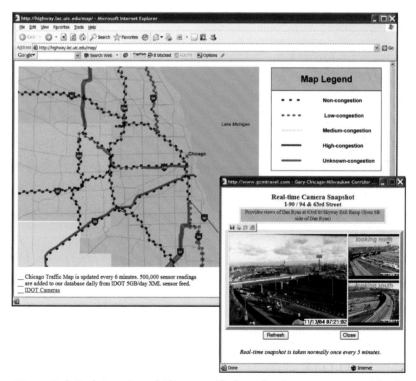

Figure 3.4*. Real-time view of Chicago traffic flows that integrates congestion levels, flow, vehicle types, video feeds, and textual accident reports.*

flow, provide visualizations that fuse this information to show the current state of the traffic network, and develop algorithms that will detect changes in the flows. Part of this project will involve characterizing normal and expected traffic patterns and developing models that will predict traffic activity when stimulus to the network occurs, as would be expected if there were a terrorist attack. The changes detected will include both changes in current congestion levels and differences in congestion levels from what would be expected from normal traffic levels.

Another example is *Smart Money* magazine's Map of the Market [Wattenberg, 1999], shown in Figure 3.5. It allows the user to monitor the performance of hundreds of stocks in real time as trading is underway. The Map of the Market uses the Treemap visualization technique [Johnson & Shneiderman, 1991; Bederson et al., 2002]. Each rectangle represents a stock (company) and the rectangle's size corresponds to the market capitalization of the company. The color of a rectangle denotes the stock's performance in a given period of time (red-decline and green-advance). The display is interactive and the viewer can easily change the segment of time being reviewed and can focus in on a particular market segment. One of the strengths of the visualization is that it provides a global impression of how the market is doing as a whole as well as the details of individual companies.

As these two examples show, real-time visualization can be a powerful tool in gaining insight from streaming data. However, real-time analytical systems for streaming data are still in their very early stages, as most visual analytics tools are targeted at static data sets.

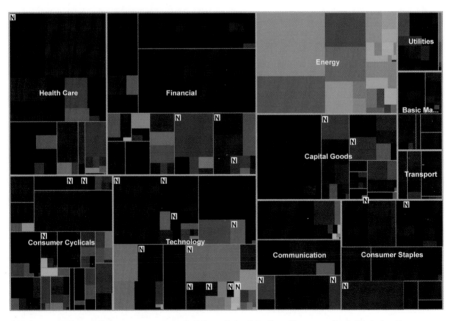

Figure 3.5. Smart Money *magazine's Map of the Market illustrates both high-level overviews and company-level details about stock market activity.*

Recommendation 3.13

Develop visual representations and new analysis techniques for streaming data, including data collected by sensors. Develop visual analytic techniques that detect and show changes in the streams and that integrate with predictive modeling tools.

The research challenge is to create a new class of visualizations for streaming data. Three significant problems must be addressed for streaming data visualizations:

1. Provide **situational awareness** for data streams.
2. Show **changes** in the state of the system and help users identify when the changes are significant.
3. **Fuse** various types of information to provide an integrated view of the information.

Visual representations by themselves are insufficient to answer many analytic questions and must integrate with algorithms for change detection, forecasting, and predictive modeling tools.

It is also important to note that these types of analysis activities rarely occur in a quiet, private setting free of interruptions or distractions. Instead, they often take place under extreme pressure in shared workspaces such as command and control centers. We need a better understanding of human attention and how it affects the analysis activities that a person may be performing. How can we facilitate an analyst acquiring the previous state in an analytic process when some interruption or distraction occurs? Can we design visualizations and systems that are more pliable to the interruptions that are bound to occur, that is, techniques that better facilitate analysts reorienting themselves and resuming prior activities?

Handling Scale

As described in Chapter 1, our ability to collect data is increasing at a faster rate than our ability to analyze it. In this section, we address the issues of visual scalability, information scalability, and software scalability that were raised in Chapter 1. Recall that visual scalability is the capability of visualization representations and visualization tools to display massive data sets effectively. Information scalability is the capability to extract relevant information from massive data streams. Software scalability is the capability of the software to accommodate data sets of varying sizes. We wish to avoid the hidden costs that arise when we build and maintain monolithic, non-interacting, non-scalable software models.

Analytic scalability is the capability of the mathematical algorithms to efficiently accommodate large data sets. As data set sizes and complexity increase, new analytical approaches and algorithms are needed that can handle the increased complexity. The computational complexity of many current visual analytics algorithms is such that these algorithms cannot process data as rapidly as they are received.

Scalability of Visual Representations

The state of the art for representing an information space typically consists of a static representation of the space that users interact with and manipulate to discover patterns within the information. The challenge is that the complexity of large information spaces can overwhelm any single representation. A new class of dynamic and scalable visual representations is needed to enable rich analysis of these information spaces.

The choice of visual representation affects visual scalability. Some visual metaphors scale well in some circumstances, while others do not. To illustrate, we describe six common visual metaphors, which are shown in Figure 3.6 using Visual Insights' ADVIZOR. These metaphors are chosen to be intentionally simple. They represent only a single dimension of the information space and illustrate one approach toward visual scalability.

Bar charts (top left in Figure 3.6) are collections of vertical bars arranged in a window. Two data attributes can be encoded in the bar height and color, and bars can be clustered or stacked to increase the number of attributes. In a bar chart, the minimum possible thickness for each bar is a single pixel, as is the minimum separation between adjacent bars. Assuming a window width of 1000 pixels, at maximum zoom a bar chart can display at most 500 bars. However, especially when there is little structure to index the bars, 50 bars is more realistic. One approach to increasing the scalability of bar charts is to employ dynamic transitions to new representation as the size and complexity of the information space increases. For example, the ADVIZOR bar chart can transition into a smoothed **histogram** (Figure 3.6, bottom right) when the number of bars exceeds the number of available pixels.

Landscapes (middle left in Figure 3.6) are a 3D version of **matrix views** (top right in Figure 3.6). They show 2D tabular data using glyphs of skyscraper-like towers arranged on a grid. Usually, as in Figure 3.6, a landscape is viewed from an angle (from straight overhead, it becomes a matrix view). The height, color, and shape of the towers can potentially encode three data attributes, depending on the nature of the attributes. For example, numerical attributes map well onto height, somewhat well onto color, and poorly onto shape. Categorical attributes map best onto color.

Landscapes can show hundreds to thousands of data elements. Limiting factors are the number of pixels used to render each 3D glyph (typically several hundred), occlusion caused by tall bars in front obscuring short bars in the back and, as for matrix views, how well the numbers of index values match the screen aspect ratio.

Relationship views (middle right in Figure 3.6) show both characteristics of individual data elements and pairwise relationships among them. Nodes correspond to data elements, whose attributes become visual characteristics such as size, color, and shape. The relationships among nodes are encoded as visual characteristics of links (width, color, pattern). For example, the network view in Figure 3.6 shows characteristics of automobile traffic in Chicago by zones (such as the central business district, the large node at the center). Node sizes are number of destination trips, and link widths show zone-to-zone flows. Network views can usefully display a graph with tens to thousands of nodes, with strong dependence on the connectivity, number of links, and inherent structure of the graph. Scalability decreases dramatically as connectivity increases, because many of the connecting links overplot,

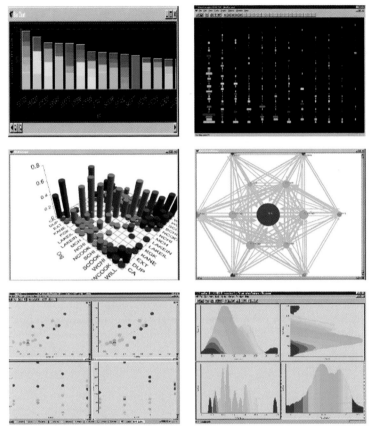

Figure 3.6. *Scalability of common visual representations. Top Left: Bar chart and Top Right: Matrix view, both illustrated with software change data. Middle Left: Landscape and Middle Right: Network view, both illustrated with zone-to-zone traffic flows in metropolitan Chicago. Lower Left: Scatterplot. Lower Right: Histogram.*

causing the display to become confusing. Graph layout algorithms that attempt to minimize overplotting can overcome this to some extent. Their effect is visual accessibility to data rather than display of structure, because distances may not encode relationships between nodes. Visual scalability is limited if layout algorithms destroy or distort "real" relationships (for example, geography) among nodes.

Scatterplots (bottom left in Figure 3.6) can display 100,000 points or more, depending on the data pattern. The primary factor limiting scatterplot scalability is point overplotting: as the number of points increases, points overplot, not only making structure in the data, such as trends or concentrations of points, harder and harder to identify, but also rendering access to details of the data impossible.

More recent work by Fekete and Plaisant [2002] has addressed the challenge of scaling visual representations. They are studying innovative approaches to represent one million discrete items visually without use of aggregation techniques. They are investigating both visual attributes and interaction techniques, such as animation, to facilitate data set exploration. Work by Munzner et al. [2003] on TreeJuxtaposer provided tools for comparing trees of several hundred thousand nodes. The visualization technique, called Accordion Drawing, has recently been extended to work on trees of up to 15 million nodes [Beermann, 2005].

Technology Needs

To scale our visual representations to meet ever-escalating data volumes, we must advance the state of the art in several major areas: visual representation of large data collections, support for multi-type information synthesis, and support for visualization of high-dimensional spaces.

Visual representation of large data collections

We need to extend the state of the art for visual representations to be able to explore heterogeneous multi-source, multi-dimensional, time-varying information streams. We must develop new visual methods to explore massive data in a time-critical manner. We must develop new methods to address the complexity of information and create a seamless integration of computational and visual techniques to create a proper environment for analysis. We must augment our methods to consider visual limits, human perception limits, and information content limits.

Recommendation 3.14

Develop a science of visual scalability that includes new ways to define it, metrics to quantify it, and techniques to increase visual representation scalability.

It is difficult to increase what we cannot measure, so the first step toward increasing visual representation scalability must be to develop ways to measure it. Current scalability metrics do not capture what is important for visual scalability. Thus we must establish metrics that allow us to evaluate both visual metaphors and data representations as they apply to scalable algorithms. The best measurement will evaluate the representations according not only to scale but also to the number of insights, actions, or value achieved for the analyst.

Existing visual representations commonly support display of several orders of magnitude less data than needed to fully represent available data. For the field of visual analytics to achieve its potential, we need to develop new representations and techniques that support display of much greater data volumes. One approach to this is to create approaches that dynamically change form as the size and complexity of the information space increases.

Visual representations to support synthesis

Synthesis includes the capability to fuse the relevant information from divergent multi-source, multi-dimensional, time-varying information streams. This is a grand challenge in visual analytics. Not only must researchers produce new visual representations and data representations for specific data types or information streams but also we must develop methods that synthesize the relevant information into a single information space and develop new visual metaphors that allow the analyst to "look inside" this complex, time-varying space.

Recommendation 3.15

Develop visual representations for information synthesis. The representations should combine relevant information from heterogeneous multi-source, multi-dimensional, time-varying information streams into a single seamless visual representation.

Many visual analytics problems will involve heterogeneous data that must be integrated, synthesized, and viewed at multiple layers. Current visual representations often focus on a single attribute and do not enable analysts to understand the richness in complex heterogeneous information spaces. New representations are needed to help analysts understand complex heterogeneous information spaces. For example, in a crisis management center, analysts need to integrate information involving geospatial locations, text, flows, weather, video feeds, and radiological sensors into a single analytic environment to support real-time emergency management.

Scaling the number of dimensions

Analysis of large information spaces often translates into the analysis of data scattered in very-high-dimensional (VHD) spaces, consisting of hundreds or thousands of variables. Interesting structures in these spaces may be nonplanar or nonlinear, suggesting that the analyst will require more sophisticated tools for analysis.

The challenges of scaling to deal with high-dimensional data affect both the visual representation and interaction techniques and the fundamental data representations and transformations that underlie those visual representations. We address the visual representation and interaction challenge here. The data representation and transformation issues are described in Chapter 4.

Recommendation 3.16

Research and develop visual representation and interaction methods for very-high-dimensional, large information spaces.

Visually representing only a couple dimensions of a high-dimensional space is not necessarily effective in conveying the important content of that space. Not only can this scaled-down representation obscure the complex relationships that may exist within the data but it can also deceive the user with its simplicity. New visual representations and interactions are needed that help represent complex relationships without oversimplifying information. For example, Yang et al. [2004] developed a visualization that represents each of the dimensions of a high-dimensional space, along with all of the values for those dimensions, in a single display. Dimensionality reduction techniques (described in Chapter 4) should go hand in hand with visual representations that help users understand the complexity of their information.

Novel Systems for Generating Visualizations

Our ability to experiment with and evaluate new interactive visual representations depends on our ability to create systems using them. This section focuses on the issues involved with the software that will create visual representations for the analyst's use.

Creating effective visualization representations is a labor-intensive process that requires a solid understanding of the visualization pipeline, characteristics of the data to be displayed, and the tasks to be performed by the analyst. Current visualization software generally has been written in environments where at least some of this necessary information was missing.

In general, it is not possible for the data analyst, who has the best understanding of the data and task, to construct new tools. The development of a visualization application requires a firm understanding of issues of perception, data, information structures, human-computer interaction, and graphics, not to mention the knowledge of the wide range of possible visual mappings available. He or she also has little time to learn how to interpret new visualizations and determine when to use them. Instead, the visual analytics community needs technology to support the rapid creation of visual methods that are tuned to the data, tasks, and users involved in the analysis.

State of the Art

There have been four general approaches for constructing visualization software. The first, and most common, is to build a general-purpose visualization tool that targets a particular domain. Examples of systems following this approach include IN-SPIRE visual text analysis software [Hetzler & Turner 2004]; OpenDx (formerly IBM Visualization Data Explorer [http://www.opendx.org]); the general-purpose AVS software [Haeberli, 1988 and http://www.avs.org]; XmdvTool [Ward, 1994] and Spotfire [http://www.spotfire.com] for multi-dimensional data; and Rivet [Bosch, 2000].

A second broad approach for constructing visualizations involves visualization toolkits. The most obvious approach is to build component-based visualization libraries such as the InfoVisToolkit [Fekete, 2004 and http://ivtk.sourceforge.net/], ILOG's library, (www.ilog.com), Visual Decisions' In3D, or AT&T Bell Laboratories' Vz. These libraries simplify software construction by providing high-level programming constructs for creating visualizations. However, programming is still required to use them.

A third related approach at a higher level of abstraction is to build visualization components that work well together. Examples of this approach include North's Snap-Together Visualizations [North et al., 2002] and Eick's ADVIZOR visualization components [Eick, 2000]. Although visual components provide more capability than object libraries, the currently available technologies are not sufficient. It is very difficult to create reusable software in general and even harder to create reusable user interface software that includes visualization software.

A fourth approach toward constructing visualizations involves systems that automatically generate visualization software. This approach includes the generation of visualizations based on creating a large database of examples that can be queried based on user needs [Zhou et al., 2002] and the use of rule-based techniques to match task and data characteristics to appropriate visualizations [Mackinlay, 1986; Roth & Mattis, 1991; Zhou, 1999]. Taxonomies of methods have also been used as a mechanism to facilitate the rapid development of effective visualizations [Chi, 2000; Fujishiro et al., 2000]. Analysis of domains [Espinoza et al., 1999], user tasks [Casner, 1991], and data characteristics [Zhou & Feiner, 1996] have also been used in the design of visual presentations.

Technology Needs

Research is needed to move beyond the current state of handcrafting special-purpose visual representations to reach a future in which visual analytics software can rapidly adapt to new data and analytical needs.

Recommendation 3.17

Develop tools and techniques to incrementally automate the common tasks involved with creating visualizations.

We believe that it will be quite difficult to provide a complete solution for the problem of generating visual representations to support visual analytics. However, we think that there is an opportunity for semi-automatic methods that help users with many of the routine tasks involved with creating visualizations. There is a vast difference in quality between visualizations created by skilled artists and those created using widely available visualization software. We need to develop incremental techniques and software to reduce this gap.

Although we need new and novel visual representations, we also need robust, easy-to-use software that implements well-known metaphors. For example, the community needs software to produce visualizations for timelines, graphs, trees, and geospatial data.

Recommendation 3.18

Develop high-quality visualization components for well-known visual representations.

Currently, each visualization system re-implements these basic visual representations at great expense and effort. We need reusable visualization components that embody well-known visual representations. In many ways, these components are like the mathematical software libraries that are now widely distributed.

We need to create the next-generation technology for producing visual analytics systems. The current generation of visual analytics tools has been developed at great expense and targets a narrow range of specific problems. To achieve their potential, visual analytics tools need to target a much broader range of problems; therefore, we must reduce the development costs to create these tools. New ideas and technologies are needed to produce these tools. We are optimistic that this is now possible with the emergence of standards such as XML and web services.

Summary

Visual representations and interaction technologies provide the mechanism for allowing the user to see and understand large volumes of information at once. Scientific principles for depicting information must provide the basis for visual representations, and principles are needed for new interaction approaches to support analytical techniques. Together, these foundations provide the basis for new visual paradigms that can scale to support analytical reasoning in many situations.

Visual design theory is more mature than interaction theory, so investments in the further development of interaction theory should take priority. Interaction theory must take into account the time constraints associated with varying levels of urgency in an analytic task. The application of visual representations and interactions must necessarily be adapted to fit the needs of the task at hand. The issues of scale also profoundly affect the design of visual representations and interactions and must be considered explicitly in the design of new visual representation and interaction techniques.

Creating effective visual representations is a labor-intensive process. We need new methods for constructing visually based systems that simplify the development process and result in better-targeted applications.

Summary Recommendations

The following high-level recommendations summarize the detailed recommendations from this chapter. These actions are necessary to advance the science of visual representations in support of visual analytics.

Recommendation

Create a science of visual representations based on cognitive and perceptual principles that can be deployed through engineered, reusable components. Visual representation principles must address all types of data, address scale and information complexity, enable knowledge discovery through information synthesis, and facilitate analytical reasoning.

Visual representations and interaction techniques provide the analyst and the first responder with their understanding of developing situations so that they may take action. A science of visual representations has been developed to support scientific applications, but different visual representations are needed to address the diverse data types that are relevant to homeland security missions. These data must be combined and presented to the user in a way that allows the user to understand their meaning, regardless of the data type or format of the original data. The goal is to expose all relevant data in a way that facilitates the reasoning process to enable action.

Recommendation

Develop a new suite of visual paradigms that support the analytical reasoning process.

These visualizations must:

- Facilitate understanding of massive and continually growing collections of data of multiple types
- Provide frameworks for analysis of spatial and temporal data
- Support understanding of uncertain, incomplete, and often misleading information
- Provide user- and task-adaptable, guided representations that enable full situation awareness while supporting development of detailed actions
- Support multiple levels of data and information abstraction
- Facilitate knowledge discovery through information synthesis, which is the integration of data based on their meaning rather than the original data type.

No one visual paradigm can address all possible tasks and situations. Therefore, we recommend developing a suite of visual paradigms that address multiple situations ranging from vulnerability analysis to real-time monitoring to emergency response support. The scale of data, especially in the forms of sensor, text, and imagery, is rapidly growing. Data are continually growing and changing, and visual representations must help analysts understand the changing nature of their data and the situations they represent. Likewise, many data are associated with a particular place and time. Representing these spatial and temporal qualities is necessary to provide analytical understanding. Furthermore, the visualization process is complicated by the need to support understanding of missing, conflicting, and deceptive information in an analytic discourse that is guided by the individual's knowledge and his or her task.

Recommendation

Develop a new science of interactions that supports the analytical reasoning process. This interaction science must provide a taxonomy of interaction techniques ranging from the low-level interactions to more complex interaction techniques and must address the challenge to scale across different types of display environments and tasks.

Interaction is the fuel for analytic discourse. Although the fundamental principles of interaction have been around for more than a decade, they do not address the needs for higher-order interaction techniques, such as task-directed or hypothesis-guided discourse, to support the analysis process. A new scientific theory and practice are critical to address the complexity of homeland security needs for analysis, prevention, and response. These interaction techniques must adapt to the particular dimensions of the analytical situation, ranging from longer-term analytical assessments to urgent and highly stressful emergency response support tasks. These interactions must be adaptable for use in platforms ranging from the large displays in emergency management control rooms to field-deployable handheld devices in the hands of first responders. This is a high priority for initial investments.

References

Agrawala M, D Phan, J Heiser, J Haymaker, J Klingner, P Hanrahan, and B Tversky. 2003. "Designing Effective Step-by-Step Assembly Instructions." *ACM Transactions on Graphics (TOG)*. 22(3):828-837.

Ahlberg C and B Shneiderman. 1994. "Visual Information Seeking: Tight Coupling of Dynamic Query Filters with Starfield Displays." In *Proceedings of CHI'94*, pp. 313-317. ACM Press, Boston.

Baddeley AD and GJ Hitch. 1974. "Working Memory." *The Psychology of Learning and Motivation*, Vol. 8, ed. GH Bower. Academic Press, New York.

Barlow T and P Neville. 2001. "Visualization for Decision Tree Analysis in Data Mining." In *Proceedings of the IEEE Symposium on Information Visualization 2001*, pp. 149-152. IEEE Computer Society, Washington, D.C.

Bartram L and C Ware. 2002. "Filtering and Brushing with Motion." In *Information Visualization* 1(1):66-79. Palgrave Macmillan, Basingstoke, New York.

Baudisch P, E Cutrell, D Robbins, M Czerwinski, P Tandler, B Bederson, and A Zierlinger. 2003. "Drag-and-Pop and Drag-and-Pick: Techniques for Accessing Remote Screen Content on Touch and Pen-Operated Systems." In *Proceedings of INTERACT 2003*, pp. 57-64.

Bederson B, B Shneiderman, and M Wattenberg. 2002. "Ordered and Quantum Treemaps: Making Effective Use of 2D Space to Display Hierarchies." *ACM Transactions on Graphics* 21(4):833-854.

Bederson B, A Clamage, M Czerwinski, and G Robertson. 2004. "DateLens: A Fisheye Calendar Interface for PDAs." *ACM Transactions on Computer-Human Interaction* 11(1):90-119.

Bederson B, J Hollan, K Perlin, J Meyer, D Bacon, and G Furnas. 1996. "Pad++: A Zoomable Graphical Sketchpad for Exploring Alternate Interface Physics." *Journal of Visual Languages and Computing* 7(1):3-31.

Beermann D, T Munzner, and G Humphreys. In Press. "Scalable, Robust Visualization of Large Trees." *Proceedings of EuroVis 2005*.

Bertin J. 1981. *Graphics and Graphic Information Processing*. Walter De Gruyter Inc., Berlin.

Bosch R, C Stolte, D Tang, J Gerth, M Rosenblum, and P Hanrahan. 2000. "Rivet: A Flexible Environment for Computer Systems Visualization." *Computer Graphics* 34(1):68-73.

Cadiz JJ, G Venolia, G Jancke, and A Gupta. 2002. "Designing and Deploying an Information Awareness Interface." In *Proceedings of the 2002 ACM Conference on Computer Supported Cooperative Work*, pp. 314-323.

Card SK, JD Mackinlay, and B Shneiderman. 1999. *Readings in Information Visualization: Using Vision to Think*. Morgan Kaufman, Los Altos, California.

Card S, T Moran, and A Newell. 1983. *The Psychology of Human-Computer Interaction*. Lawrence Erlbaum Associates, Hillsdale, New Jersey.

Casner S. 1999. "A Task-Analytical Approach to the Automated Design of Graphic Presentations." *ACM Transactions on Graphics* 10(2):111-151.

Chi E. 2000. "A Taxonomy of Visualization Techniques Using the Data State Reference Model." In *Proceedings of the IEEE Symposium on Information Visualization 2000*, pp. 69-75.

Cleveland WS. 1985. *The Elements of Graphing Data*. Hobart Press, Summit, New Jersey.

Cleveland W and M McGill. 1984. "Graphical Perception: Theory, Experimentation and Application to the Development of Graphical Methods." *Journal of the American Statistical Association* 79(387):531-554.

Dent BD. 1999. *Cartography: Thematic Map Design*. Wm. C. Brown Publishers, Dubuque, Iowa.

Eick SG. 2000. "Visual Discovery and Analysis." *IEEE Transactions on Visualization and Computer Graphics*. 6(1):44-58.

Eick SG, JL Steffen, and EE Sumner. 1992. "Seesoft – A Tool for Visualizing Line Oriented Software Statistics." *IEEE Transactions on Software Engineering* 18(11):957-968.

Espinosa O, C Hendrickson, and G Garrett Jr. 1999. "Domain Analysis: A Technique to Design a User-Centered Visualization Framework." In *Proceedings of the 1999 IEEE Symposium on Information Visualization 1999 (InfoVis 99)*, pp. 44-52.

Fekete J. 2004. "The InfoVis Toolkit." In *Proceedings of the 10th IEEE Symposium on Information Visualization (InfoVis'04)*, pp. 167-174. IEEE Press, Piscataway, New Jersey.

Fekete J and C Plaisant. 2002. "Interactive Information Visualization of a Million Items." In *Proceedings of the IEEE Symposium on Information Visualization (InfoViz 2002)*, pp. 117-124. IEEE Computer Society, Washington, D.C.

Finger R and A Bisantz. 2002. "Utilizing Graphical Formats to Convey Uncertainty in a Decision-Making Task." *Theoretical Issues in Ergonomic Science* 3(1):1-25.

Foley J. 2000. "Getting There: The Top Ten Problems Left." *IEEE Computer Graphics and Applications 20(1)*:66-68.

Fujishiro I, R Furuhata, Y Ichikawa, and Y Takeshima. 2000. "GADGET/IV: A Taxonomic Approach to Semi-Automatic Design of Information Visualization Applications Using Modular Visualization Environment." In *Proceedings of the IEEE Symposium on Information Visualization 2000*, pp. 77-83. IEEE Computer Society, Washington, D.C.

Furnas G. 1986. "Generalized Fisheye Views." In *Proceedings of SIGCHI Conference on Human Factors in Computing Systems*, pp. 16-23. ACM Press, New York.

Gamma E, R Helm, R Johnson, and J Vlissides. 1994. *Design Patterns: Elements of Reusable Object-Oriented Software*. Addison-Wesley, Reading, Massachusetts.

Greenberg S and M Rounding. 2001. "The Notification Collage: Posting Information to Public and Personal Displays." In *Proceedings of SIGCHI Conference on Human Factors in Computing Systems*, pp. 515-521. ACM Press, New York.

Greene S, G Marchionini, C Plaisant, and B Shneiderman. 2000. "Previews and Overviews in Digital Libraries: Designing Surrogates to Support Visual Information-Seeking." *Journal of the American Society for Information Science* 51(3):380-393.

Haeberli P. 1988. "ConMan: A Visual Programming Language for Interactive Graphics." *Proceedings of the 15th Annual Conference on Computer Graphics and Interactive Techniques*, pp. 103-111. ACM Press, New York.

Hauptmann AG and P McAvinney. 1993. "Gestures with Speech for Graphics Manipulation." *International Journal of Man-Machine Studies* 38:231-249.

Haykin S, ed. 2000. *Unsupervised Adaptive Filtering*. Wiley-Interscience, New York.

Heiser J, D Phan, M Agrawala, B Tversky, and P Hanrahan. 2004. "Identification and Validation of Cognitive Design Principles for Automated Generation of Assembly Instructions." In *Proceedings of the Working Conference on Advanced Visual Interfaces*, pp. 311-319. ACM Press, New York.

Hetzler E and A Turner. 2004. "Analysis Experiences Using Information Visualization." *IEEE Computer Graphics and Applications* 24(5):22-26.

Heuer RJ. 1999. *Psychology of Intelligence Analysis*. U.S. Government Printing Office, Washington, D.C.

Hutchings D and J Stasko. 2004. "Shrinking Window Operations for Expanding Display Space." In *Proceedings of Advanced Visual Interfaces*, pp. 350-353. ACM Press, New York.

Johnson B and B Shneiderman. 1991. "Tree-Maps: A Space Filling Approach to the Visualization of Hierarchical Information Structures." In *Proceedings of the 2nd IEEE Conference on Visualization '91*, pp. 284-291, 1991, San Diego, California. IEEE Computer Society, Washington, D.C.

Kapler T and W Wright. 2004. "GeoTime Information Visualization." *IEEE InfoVis 2004*. Oculus Info Inc. Available at http://www.oculusinfo.com/papers/KaplerWright_GeoTime_InfoViz_Final_Conf.pdf.

Kinsbourne M and RE Hicks. 1978. "Functional Cerebral Space; a Model for Overflow, Transfer and Interference Effects in Human Performance: a Tutorial Review." In *Attention and Performance VII*, ed. J Requin. Lawrence Erlbaum Associates, Hillsdale, New Jersey.

Kollin J. 1993. "A Retinal Display for Virtual-Environment Applications." In *Proceedings of SID-International Symposium, Digest of Technical Papers*, pp. 827.

MacEachren AM. 1995. *How Maps Work: Representation, Visualization and Design*. The Guilford Press, New York.

Mackinlay J. 1986. "Automating the Design of Graphical Presentations of Relational Information." *ACM Transactions on Graphics* 5(2):110-141.

Martin GL. 1989. "The Utility of Speech Input in User-Computing Interfaces." *International Journal of Man-Machine Studies* 30:355-375.

Mooshage O, H Distelmaier, and M Grandt. 2002. "Human Centered Decision Support for Anti-Air Warfare on Naval Platforms." In *Proceedings of the RTO HFM Symposium on the Role of Humans in Intelligent and Automated Systems*, RTO/NATO 2002 RTO-MP.

Munzner T, G Guimbretiere, S Tasiran, L Zhang, and Y Zhou. 2003. "TreeJuxtaposer: Scalable Tree Comparison Using Focus+Context with Guaranteed Visibility." *ACM Transactions on Graphics* 22(3):453-462. ACM Press, New York.

Newell A. 1990. *Unified Theories of Cognition*. Harvard Press, Cambridge, Massachusetts.

Norman DA. 1993. *Things That Make Us Smart: Defending Human Attributes in the Age of the Machine*. Perseus Books, New York.

North C, N Conklin, K Indukuri, and V Saini. 2002. "Visualization Schemas and a Web-Based Architecture for Custom Multiple-View Visualization of Multiple-Table Databases." *Information Visualization* 1(3/4):211-228. Palgrave MacMillan, Basingstoke, New York.

Oviatt SL. 1999. "Ten Myths of Multimodal Interaction." *Communications of the ACM* 42(11):74-81.

Plaisant C, D Carr, and B Shneiderman. March 1995. "Image-Browser Taxonomy and Guidelines for Designers." *IEEE Software* 12(2):21-32.

Rheingans P and DS Ebert. 2002. "Volume Illustration: Non-Photorealistic Rendering of Volume Models." *IEEE Transactions on Visualization and Computer Graphics* 7(3):253-265.

Robertson G, K Cameron, M Czerwinski, and D Robbins. 2002. "Animated Visualization of Multiple Intersecting Hierarchies." *Journal of Information Visualization* 1(1):50-65.

Robertson G, M Czerwinski, K Larson, D Robbins, D Thiel and M van Dantzich. 1998. "Data Mountain: Using Spatial Memory for Document Management." In *Proceedings of the 11th Annual ACM Symposium on User Interface Software and Technology*, pp. 153-162. ACM Press, New York.

Robertson G, E Horvitz, M Czerwinski, P Baudisch, DR Hutchings, B Meyers, D Robbins, and G Smith. 2004. "Scalable Fabric: Flexible Task Management." In *Proceedings of the Working Conference on Advanced Visual Interfacesence*, pp. 85-89. ACM Press, New York.

Rogowitz BE and LA Treinish. 1993. "An Architecture for Perceptual Rule-Based Visualization." In *Proceedings of the 4th IEEE Conference on Visualization*, pp. 236-243.

Roth S and J Mattis. 1991. "Automating the Presentation of Information." In *Proceedings of the IEEE Conference on Artificial Intelligence Applications*, pp. 90-97.

Sharp Systems of America. 2004. "Sharp's 3D LCD Technology Now Available for Desktop Computers." Available at http://www.sharpsystems.com/news/press_releases/release.asp?press=59.

Shneiderman B. 1996. "The Eyes Have It: A Task by Data Type Taxonomy for Information Visualizations." In *Proceedings of the 1996 IEEE Symposium on Visual Languages*, pp. 336-343. IEEE Computer Society, Washington, D.C.

Smallman H, M St. John, H Oonk, and M Cowen. 2001. "SYMBICONS: A Hybrid Symbology That Combines the Best Elements of SYMBOLS and ICONS." In *Proceedings of the 45th Annual Meeting of the Human Factors and Ergonomics Society*, pp. 114-119.

Smith S, RD Bergeron, and G Grinstein. 1990. "Stereophonic and Surface Sound Generation for Exploratory Data Analysis." In *Proceedings of the SIGCHI Conference on Human Factors in Computing Systems: Empowering People*, pp. 125-132. ACM Press, New York.

Spence R. 2000. *Information Visualization*. ACM Press, New York.

Stasko J, T Miller, Z Pousman, C Plaue, and O Ullah. 2004. "Personalized Peripheral Information Awareness Through Information Art." In *Proceedings of UbiComp (2004)*, pp. 18-35.

Stolte C, D Tang, and P Hanrahan. 2002. "Polaris: A System for Query, Analysis and Visualization of Multidimensional Relational Databases." *IEEE Transactions on Visualization and Computer Graphics* 8(1):52-65.

Svakhine N and DS Ebert. 2003. "Interactive Volume Illustration and Feature Halos." *Pacific Graphics 2003*.

Tang CW and SA Van Slyke. 1987. "Organic Electroluminescent Diodes." *Applied Physics Letters* 51(12):913-915.

Treisman A and A Davies A. 1973. "Divided Attention to Ear and Eye." pp. 101-117 in *Attention and Performance IV*, ed. S Kornblum. Academic Press, New York and London.

Tufte E. 1983. *The Visual Display of Quantitative Information*. Graphics Press, Cheshire, Connecticut.

Tufte E. 1990. *Envisioning Information*. Graphics Press, Cheshire, Connecticut.

Tufte E. 1997. *Visual Explanations: Images and Quantities, Evidence and Narrative*. Graphics Press, Cheshire, Connecticut.

Tukey JW. 1977. *Exploratory Data Analysis*. Addison-Wesley, Reading, Massachusetts.

Tversky B, JB Morrison, and M Betrancourt. 2002. "Animation: Can It Facilitate?" *International Journal of Human-Computer Studies* 57:247-262. Academic Press Inc., Duluth, Minnesota.

van Dam A. 2001. "User Interfaces: Disappearing, Dissolving and Evolving." *Communications of the ACM* 44(3):50-52.

Wang JF, GE Jabbour, EA Mash, J Anderson, Y Zhang, PA Lee, NR Armstrong, N Peyghambarian, and B Kippelen. 1999. "Oxadiazole Metal Complex for Organic Light-Emitting Diodes." *Advanced Materials* 11(15):1266-1269.

Ward MO. 1994. "XmdvTool: Integrating Multiple Methods for Visualizing Multivariate Data." In *Proceedings of the Conference on Visualization '94*, pp. 326-333. IEEE Computer Society Press, Los Alamitos, California.

Ware C. 2000. *Information Visualization: Perception for Design*. Academic Press, distributor. Published by Morgan Kaufmann, San Francisco.

Wattenberg M. 1999. "Visualizing the Stock Market." In *Proceedings of SICGHI '99 Extended Abstracts*, pp. 188-189, Pittsburgh, Pennsylvania.

Wickens CD. 1980. "The Structure of Attentional Resources." In *Attention and Performance VIII*, eds. R Nickerson and R Pew. Lawrence Erlbaum Associates, Hillsdale, New Jersey.

Wilkinson L. 1999. *The Grammar of Graphics*. Springer-Verlag, New York.

Woodruff A, J Landay, and M Stonebraker. 1998. "Constant Density Visualizations of Non-Uniform Distributions of Data." In *Proceedings of the 11th Annual ACM Symposium on User Interface Software and Technology*, pp. 19-28. ACM Press, New York.

Yang J, A Patro, S Huang, N Mehta, MO Ward, A Elke, and E Rundensteiner. 2004. "Value and Relation Display for Interactive Exploration of High Dimensional Datasets." In *Proceedings of the IEEE Symposium on Information Visualization 2004 (InfoVis 2004)*, pp. 73-80. IEEE Computer Society, Washington, D.C.

Zhou M. 1999. "Visual Planning: A Practical Approach to Automated Visual Presentation." In *Proceedings of the Sixteenth International Joint Conference on Artificial Intelligence*, pp. 634-641.

Zhou M and S Feiner. 1996. "Data Characterization for Automatically Visualizing Heterogeneous Information." In *Proceedings of the 1996 IEEE Symposium on Information Visualization*, pp. 13-20. IEEE Computer Society, Washington, D.C.

Zhou M, M Chen, and Y Feng. 2002. "Building a Visual Database for Example-Based Graphics Generation." In *Proceedings of the 2002 IEEE Symposium on Information Visualization*, pp. 23-30. IEEE Computer Society, Washington, D.C.

"With me everything turns into mathematics."
—Rene Descartes (1596-1650)

Data Representations and Transformations

Visual analytics is fueled by data. These data must be represented, combined, and transformed to enable users to detect the expected and discover the unexpected. The volume and complexity of data, combined with their dynamic nature, provide a strong motivation to create innovative and scalable approaches to transformation and representation.

What Are Data Representations and Transformations?

To permit visualization, analysis, and reporting, data must be transformed from their original raw state into a form, or representation, that is suitable for manipulation. These data representations and transformations are the foundation on which visual analytics is built.

Data representations are structured forms suitable for computer-based transformations. These structures must exist in the original data or be derivable from the data themselves. They must retain the information and knowledge content and the related context within the original data to the greatest degree possible.

The structures of underlying data representations are generally neither accessible nor intuitive to the user of the visual analytics tool. They are frequently more complex in nature than the original data and are not necessarily smaller in size than the original data. The structures of the data representations may contain hundreds or thousands of dimensions and be unintelligible to a person, but they must be transformable into lower-dimensional representations for visualization and analysis.

Data representations may illuminate key features in the data, rather than showing every detail, so they are important to the process of data abstraction. The degree to which a visual analytics software tool can address the challenges of scale is also influenced by the data representation selected by the tool developer.

Data representations underlie the interactive visualizations described in Chapter 3. The creation of appropriate data representations is essential to producing meaningful visual representations. The data representation method must facilitate the analytical reasoning methods and capture the intermediate and final results of the reasoning processes described in Chapter 2. These analytical results must be communicated via the production, presentation, and dissemination processes described in Chapter 5.

A *data transformation* is a mathematical procedure that converts data into different representations that may provide more insight for an analyst. Data transformations are required to convert data into structured forms that permit them to be visualized and analyzed. Data transformations are used to augment data by deriving additional data. For example, clustering is used to organize data into groups. Data transformations convert data into new and meaningful forms. For example, linguistic analysis can be used to assign meaning to the words in a text document. Data transformations make it possible to create more useful visual representations that support more sophisticated analyses. Data transformations can be applied iteratively, with each transformation producing a new representation and potentially leading to new insights. Data transformations may be used to find convenient layouts for displays, such as by creating a low-dimensional display space from a high-dimensional data space.

A major challenge of visual analytics is to find the most useful ways to couple data transformations with interactive visual representations and analytical reasoning techniques. Data representation and transformation techniques should not introduce biases that would affect the analytic conclusions based on the data. At the same time, they should preserve the inherent biases, uncertainties, and other quality attributes of the original data.

Currently, within visual analytics, the sources for data representation and transformation are primarily within the areas of mathematics and statistics, modeling and simulation, and natural language processing (NLP). Generally, much of the knowledge representation work going on in the area of information sciences and technology has some accompanying structure that can be leveraged for automatically generating visual representations and supporting analysis. Without this structure, analytical options are limited because computer processing is constrained.

Transformations to Support Visual Representation

To facilitate the analysis of large and intrinsically complex data repositories, data transformations can be used not only to generate raw analysis results but also to generate representations that can be mapped into spatial representations.

The task of creating representations and transformations to support visualization builds on the foundational work of Euclid (325 to 265 BC, relative to his treatise, *The Elements*) and of Rene Descartes (AD 1596 to 1650, inventor of analytic geometry, i.e., the Cartesian coordinate system). For every point we represent as a pixel on the screen, we leverage Euclid's and Descartes' visions and creativity [Bell, 1965].

In combining geometry and analytics to generate a point on a screen, we must have a value on the horizontal axis (x) and a value on the vertical axis (y). For example, to represent an individual as a point on the screen, we must have some associated spatial structure, say weight, x = 165 pounds, and height, y = 71 inches, thus yielding a location on the screen, or a point in the appropriate visualization space.

About This Chapter

The field of data representations and transformations is so large that it cannot be addressed completely here. Instead, we describe some representative examples and address the data representation and transformation topics that are most central to the advancement of visual analytics. We focus this chapter primarily on representations and transformations to support the creation of visual representations for analysis. The methods described in this chapter also address some of the needs for capturing and presenting the artifacts of the analytical reasoning process. These topics are described in more depth in Chapters 2 and 5.

We identify the need for research in data representation and transformation to better facilitate visual analytics. We highlight areas that must be pursued to address the challenges of understanding complex, diverse, dynamic, and uncertain data.

We also describe the research needed to deal with the linguistic and culturally related structure associated with language data. These data must undergo transformation before they can be represented in a way that supports visualization and analysis. The levels of linguistic structure inform the representation of language data, and some text transformations enrich the semantics of the resulting visualization. Culture affects language data, which in turn affect the visualization of language data, but the community is only in the early stages of research into data transformations to account for these cultural effects.

Because the analytic process often involves the comprehensive consideration of data of multiple types and sources, we present a discussion of the need for synthesizing this diverse information into a single environment in which it can be analyzed. The goal is to allow the analyst to focus on understanding the meaning of the information, rather than being burdened by artificial constraints associated with the form in which the information was originally packaged.

Data Representations

Data come in a variety of types, and each type must be represented in ways that facilitate computational transformations to yield analytical insight. Visualizations that combine multiple types of data are also needed to support comprehensive analytic reasoning in certain situations.

Analytic insights can hinge on the proper data representation underlying the visual representation. The data representation must faithfully preserve the inherent structure of the data as well as the data's real-world context and meaning. In most cases, that inherent structure will be known for a given data source. For example, a given sensor will produce data in a consistent format. If it is unknown, then technical analysis must be done to choose the proper representation for the data. It is important for the data representation to portray the quality of the data as collected. If information is missing, purposefully hidden, or misleading, the analyst must be able to detect that.

Data may be characterized from multiple perspectives, each of which has a bearing on the data representation:

- **Data type**. Data may be numeric, non-numeric, or both. Numeric data often originate from sensors or computerized instruments, and the scientific community has developed a variety of techniques for representing these data. Non-numeric data can include anything from language data, such as textual news stories, to categorical, image, or video data. Although techniques and formats exist for representing individual elements of the raw data, techniques for representing the key features or content of the data are far less mature.

- **Level of structure**. Data may range from completely structured, such as categorical data, to semi-structured, such as an e-mail message containing information about sender and receiver along with free-form text, to completely unstructured, such as a narrative description on a web page. The term *unstructured* does not mean that the data are without pattern, but rather that they are expressed in such a way that only humans can meaningfully interpret their construct. Structure provides information that can be interpreted to determine data organization and meaning. It provides a consistent context for the information. The inherent structure in data can form a basis for data representation. Unstructured data lack the same clues for automatic interpretation for data. Any structure to be applied to the data must be derived in some way.

- **Geospatial characteristics**. When data are associated with a particular location or region, this information must be represented. Any type of data, whether numeric data from a specific sensor, textual data, or image data from a specific satellite, may have a geospatial association.

- **Temporal characteristics**. Some data, such as reference data, are static and not presumed to change over time. However, data of all types may have a temporal association, and this association may be either discrete or continuous.

This section provides a high-level description of some of the considerations associated with representing data of varying types, levels of structure, and temporal and geospatial characteristics. Note that none of these data characteristics can truly be considered independently of the others. All facets must be considered collectively, in conjunction with knowledge about the structure of the source and limitations of the data-gathering technology, to create an appropriate representation. Here, we address some of the elements of data representation that are most significant with respect to visual analytics, but this only scratches the surface of the work that has been done by the computer science community in data representation.

Numeric Data

Numeric data are those data that are quantitative and result from sensors or other instruments, including other computers. These data are unique because they are produced by instruments that automatically format their data and may also be accompanied by software that collects and stores the output as data are being produced. Depending on the analytic tools available, these data may or may not require additional manipulation and re-representation before visually based analysis can begin.

Numeric data have long been the focus of data representation methods, even for manual analysis. There are classical computer-based methods for numeric data representation, many of which reduce the amount or complexity of the data. The current pervasiveness of massive collections of numeric data, such as high-energy physics data [Jacobsen, 2004] and data from the Earth Observation Satellites (EOS) [Braverman, 2004], has spurred development of data representation techniques. These classical techniques provide a basis on which visual analytics can build.

Under normal operational conditions, numeric data would be scientifically analyzed using computational tools designed for the formatted input being received. Research efforts may include investigation of analytic techniques to determine the data structure, the quality of the data source, or predictive indicators. However, the research may also focus on the methods used to represent the data or to detect and mitigate formatting errors in the data.

In emergency conditions and other situations where speed is critical, data representation may play a significant role in making massive data cognitively available to the analyst. Any methods used at this stage in the processing must make special effort to represent the original data content as faithfully as possible so as not to mislead the analyst.

Representing or modeling numeric data appropriately is the key to solving problems. Appropriate numeric data representations and transformations allow the visual representations to speed the analytic process.

Language Data

Linguistically organized data encompass all data that represent human language. While language data are typically processed in textual form, they may also be derived from sound waves or images. Regardless of the original source, representation of the language data content presents many common challenges.

It is difficult to automatically interpret even well-edited English text as well as a native English-speaking reader would understand the text. However, there have been advances in NLP of printed, spoken, and scanned forms in multiple languages that can make a difference in the visual analysis of large amounts of data. In this section, we address the representation of language data. In a later section, the transformation of these representations will be addressed to semantically enrich the resulting visual representation.

Language data can be processed without any acknowledgment of their linguistic structure because meaning is inherent in the communication of the originator. The originator intended to communicate a message to an audience, so the language can be presumed to be meaningful to the reader without automated linguistic analysis. So-called "bag of words" methods, in which a document is treated as a collection of words occurring with some frequency, work because they do not obscure this inherent meaning when presented to the analyst. For many analytic purposes, these methods are ideal. The first mechanized methods were developed by Salton [1968] for information retrieval, and his work continues to be foundational to all language processing as well as other inherently meaning-bearing sources of data [Salton et al., 1975]. His work on identifying salient terms in a corpus, indexing, and constructing high-dimensional signature vectors that represent a corpus' topics or articles remains key to most of the current effective tools for analyzing large volumes of text. High-dimensional vectors can be projected into 2D to 3D representations to support visualizations that analysts can navigate.

In addition to Salton's work, centuries of general linguistic study of language provide a foundation for the computer-based analysis of language. The general structure of language provides a framework for the eventual reduction of text to its meaningful logical form for computer-based analysis. While computer-based linguistic analysis is not a solved problem, current capabilities provide some reliable results that add semantic richness to the "bag of words" approach.

Linguistics defines the levels of structure based on analysis across and within languages, and computational linguistics provides the methods for assigning structure to textual data. As shown in Figure 4.1, the major levels of structure applicable here are phonological, morphological, syntactic, semantic, and the pragmatic (or discourse) level.

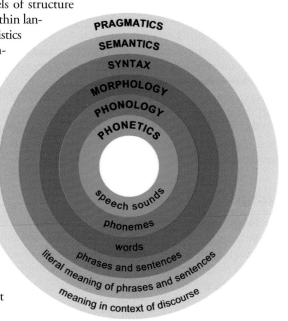

The *phonological level* deals with the structure of the sounds that convey linguistic content in a language. However, this level of structure applies to writing and sign language as well. It is basically the lowest level containing the elements that distinguish meaning and can be defined physically as a

Figure 4.1. Major levels of linguistic structure

means of linguistic production. Each language has its own set of sounds that are used in words to convey meaning at any time in its history. These elements are not usually equivalent to the graphemic elements (the smallest elements of meaning) in the writing system. Instead, phonological elements are related to graphemic elements by rules, to a greater or lesser degree. The graphemic system can influence the phonological system. For example, in Mongolia, the Russians replaced the Mongolian script with the Cyrillic alphabet, which caused a change in the vowel harmony rules of the spoken language because the full set of vowels in their verbal context could not be represented in Cyrillic. Usually, however, the phonological system is thought to dominate the written system.

The *morphological level* of a language is the level at which meaning can be assigned to parts of words and the level that describes how morphemes (the smallest meaning elements of words) are combined to make a word. Some written systems, such as

English and Chinese, are morphological in nature. For example, the morpheme "sign" is not always pronounced the same way in English words in which it appears (*sign, signal, signature, resign, resignation*). In highly agglutinative languages, words are built by affixing morphemes to one another, making word boundaries sparse within sentences. In such languages, such as Turkish and many Native American languages, an entire sentence can appear in one word. Obviously, this fact plays havoc with the "bag of words" approach because word boundaries are not easily identifiable using information within the corpus. Even in non-agglutinative languages, segmentation may be required because of the written system's lack of word delimitation. Chinese is such a language.

The *syntactic level* of structure concerns the structure of the sentence, i.e., the categories of words and the order in which they are assembled to form a grammatical sentence. The categories used in syntax are known as parts of speech. The main parts of speech are nouns and verbs. Verbs govern the roles that the nouns in the sentence can play, and the ordering and/or case marking of nouns determine their roles. Roles can be characterized at various levels. Most commonly, the syntactic roles are those like subject and object. The roles can also be viewed with degrees of semantic content, such as agent, instrument, or location.

The predicate-argument structure of the sentence is used to represent the logical form of the sentence, which is a semantic representation. The *semantic level* of structure of the sentence is computationally defined to be the level of representation supporting inferencing and other logical operations. Within linguistic theory, Montague semantics was one of the bases for this approach [Montague, 1974].

Other representations important to the semantic level include, but are not limited to, the meanings of the words. Lexicology is as old as writing, perhaps older, but modern lexicology includes psycholinguistic knowledge concerning how the brain stores the words in memory. WordNet is the preeminent lexicon structured along psycholinguistic principles [Miller, 1998]. The utility of WordNet for computational linguistics has been immeasurable. It contains an ontology, or hierarchical structuring, of the words of English and allows the user to find synonyms, antonyms, hypernyms (more general terms), and hyponyms (more specific terms). It also distinguishes the sense of the words. Other languages have WordNets developed for them and the senses of the words have been linked cross-lingually for use in sense disambiguation within and across languages (see EuroWordNet at http://www.illc.uva.nl/EuroWordNet/).

The *discourse structure* of language is the level of structure of the exchange or presentation of information in a conversation or a written piece. It describes the principles and order of information in the exchange.

All of these levels of structure are opportunities for linguistic representation that could support visualization. Advances like the language-independent UNICODE encoding standard are important at a very basic level, because visual analytics data representations must support analysis of multilingual data. However, the problems of assigning a structure to text are not solved by any means. The real issue is how useful the available linguistic representations are in creating data representations to support visualization and analysis. Techniques, such as tokenization and segmentation, morphology/stemming, and part-of-speech tagging, are sufficiently advanced to provide value in the representation of textual data. None of these techniques are perfect, but all can be leveraged for many languages of interest. Still other techniques, such as automatic speech transcription, optical character recognition, and handwriting recognition, are currently adequate only under ideal conditions (high-fidelity input equipment, rich contextual clues, and lack of noise in the original expression or signal).

Image and Video Data

The largest volume of data is generally agreed to come in the form of imagery. Images come from a large number of sources, including satellites, surveillance cameras, professional and amateur photojournalism, microscopes, telescopes, and other visual instruments. In addition to the large volume, there is also the possibility of deception because of the tools widely available for editing digital imagery. There is a vast array of research underway in aspects of image and video analysis. Rather than cataloguing this work here, we focus on the particular areas of most significant concern for visual analytics.

State-of-the-art image processing allows edge detection, identification of regions of interest [Glassner, 1995], and the reconstruction of 3D objects from a set of still pictures [Debevec, 1996]. The state of the art in automatic imagery analysis has largely been achieved for computer vision, especially in robotic applications.

The key challenge for visual analytics is to derive semantic content or meaning from images in real time. We must make the leap from the representation of the image itself to the representation of the information contained in the image. The exploding volume of available imagery will stretch data storage and processing limitations. To realize value from these data, the potentially important content must be derived from the data rapidly and accurately so that unneeded data may be discarded and the remaining data can be compressed and offloaded to less accessible storage hardware.

Thus far, good results have only been achieved when the general domain of the imagery is understood, such as face matching and identification of military objects. Inferring that a set of pixels is a particular object in a scene from an unknown source has not been adequately addressed. This is an area of active research. Novel techniques used for massive textual data have shown promise in handling imagery. Ilgen et al. [2000] have applied their vector approach to imagery producing a pixel vector. The method may be useful for identification and verification of objects as well as corrupted images. The detection of hidden messages in imagery is in its infancy [Johnson et al., 2000]. Only under special internet transmission conditions has this been a problem up until now.

Video data are imagery sequences with an associated temporal dimension. Although not routinely exploited today, this temporal dimension can be useful in automated analysis of scenes and identification of objects and events. Research progress has been made in analyzing video content. Capabilities exist to search through and organize large video libraries (see the Virage website at http://www.virage.com/products/). Work has been done to partition video into key sequences [Kasik, 2004], and several companies are working on techniques to index videos for quick retrieval and review.

The proper representation of image and video for analysis is critical to homeland security. We must gain leverage from the extensive research and development efforts already underway in this field to advance the capability to represent not just the image or video itself but also the meaning it contains.

Structural Characteristics of Data

The level of structure within data directly affects their representation. In general, numeric data are well-structured. Imagery have their own unique structure, but the information content within the image is implicit and thus without inherent structure. Language data may exist in forms that range from highly structured to completely unstructured.

Often, metadata exist to describe a particular data element, such as information about the source of an image. These metadata are generally of a known structure. Categorical data, such as survey data, may contain a mix of language data and numeric data, but are also highly structured.

One important example of structured data is transaction data. Transaction data are highly structured records that document an individual event, such as a telephone call or a border crossing. Transaction data contain very small amounts of information in each record and generally do not have a clear context. However, transaction data are generally voluminous. Businesses use transaction data for many purposes, including tracking buying patterns and identifying potential credit card fraud. Security and privacy protection are especially important concerns for working with transaction data.

Many types of data lack the structure that is apparent in transaction data. When structure is not apparent within data, it must be identified through the use of innovative data transformations. Data transformations are discussed in more detail in the remainder of this chapter. When structure exists within data or metadata, that structure must be preserved and represented. Structured data are generally formatted as a field name followed by one or more field values of a specific type. The classic representation of structured data is a set of relations stored in a relational database management system (RDBMS). RDBMSs form the backbone of the commercial database industry. Significant investments have been made in relational databases, and large amounts of data are stored in such databases.

The selected data representation has significant influence over its range of possible analytic uses. In the case of a database, the schema describing field names and types is one such data representation. When possible, schema design should be done knowing the analytic uses to which the data will be put.

For example, the schemas for most databases are designed with transactional efficiency in mind. Names are normally replaced with unique numeric identifiers to avoid the issue of duplicate names. Databases are also normalized so that updates can be done efficiently. However, information shown to an analyst must be represented in the most meaningful way, using familiar names rather than obscure identifiers. There are tools that support the transformation or mapping of one schema into another. However, until recently, schema-mapping tools have not scaled well to large schemas or mappings [Robertson et al., 2005]. The size and complexity of databases for homeland security applications of visual analytics will grow so large that new techniques will need to be developed to support schema mapping in the cases where analytic uses are not fully known at the time the database schemas are designed. Object-oriented database structures add flexibility but also are not easily changed after an analytic suite of tools is developed. Document metadata also suffer from the same representational limitations.

Another limitation of traditional RDBMSs is that their performance is optimized for transactions per second rather than analytical queries per second. The types of queries used for analysis are quite different. Rather than searching for and updating a single record, analysis usually requires scanning the entire database to find complex relationships of interest. During the scan, filters are applied, aggregations computed, and other calculations performed. In the commercial sector, this has led to a new class of database systems called online analytical processing (OLAP) systems that pre-compute aggregates and support more complex calculations and data modeling.

Interactive analytic workloads are different from traditional queries for other reasons. For example, most analysis is incremental. A subsequent query is a refinement of a previous query. Data management and caching, as well as query optimizers, could be improved to support analysis. Major breakthroughs are needed in these areas to support analytics.

Geospatial Characteristics of Data

Geospatial phenomena have a number of distinguishing characteristics.

First, natural boundaries tend to be very convoluted and irregular, and as a result do not lend themselves to compact definition or mathematical prediction. Geospatial databases tend to quickly become large as a result because of the detailed coordinate data that must be stored.

Second, geospatial phenomena tend to be scale-specific, and phenomena at different scales are interrelated. For example, global weather patterns affect the occurrence of excessive rain in California, which affects the risk of local landslides. Often, problems must be considered at multiple resolutions simultaneously. For example, in detection of a disease epidemic, information may need to be considered at the level of individual hospitals, at the city, state, and national levels in order to identify pockets of illness and identify both localized and widespread outbreaks. Accommodating the multi-resolution nature of geospatial data is a research challenge.

Third, locational definitions of geospatial entities are often inexact and can be scale or context dependent. For example, the boundaries between specific vegetation types in any given area and the location of shorelines when examining at a very local scale are conceptually transition zones and not sharp boundaries. If viewing the same information from a state-wide or national scale, these boundaries would most often be viewed as discrete. City boundaries are also fuzzy transition zones if seen from the point of view of an economist, but cities do have sharply defined boundaries for the purpose of political jurisdiction.

Fourth, locations are commonly recorded using specialized Cartesian, spherical, or other types of coordinate systems including latitude and longitude, Universal Transverse Mercator (UTM) grids, township and range, or street addresses. Location expressed in some of these coordinate systems cannot be converted algorithmically into other systems with a predictable degree of accuracy, such as the conversion of street addresses into latitude and longitude. This often forces the storage of more than one type of coordinate for entities within the same database. Not only does this make the required storage volumes even larger but it also presents an additional level of complexity in maintaining the integrity of the database as data are added and updated.

The combination of these properties makes representation of geospatial data particularly difficult. Boundaries are represented as sharp demarcations in currently used data models in part because of the discrete nature of computing hardware. An additional problem arises in the transformation of a space that is inherently multidimensional into computer memory, which is normally one-dimensional in nature. Representation of geospatial phenomena in a way that retains their essential nature has proven to be a particularly challenging problem [Burrough & Frank, 1995; Mark et al., 1999; Peuquet, 2002; Yuan et al., 2004].

Although relational databases provide significant flexibility for representing many types of data, this does not extend into the geospatial realm, and we still lack representational techniques that are up to the task of modern requirements for visual or quantitative analysis of such data. It is a well-known principle that how the data are represented determines what can and cannot be done effectively with those data. Data representations can also suggest approaches for visual display. A classic example is the use of sequenced snapshots as a data model for storing space-time data; this model coincides with the visual representation of "digital movies"—a series of still images shown in quick succession to visually display movement and change through space-time.

The two basic representation schemes used currently for geospatial data (raster grids and vector) operate as independent and distinct representations within current geospatial data-handling systems. Most current commercial geographic information system (GIS) tools use a multi-representational database design and incorporate both raster- and vector-type representations for coordinate data, as well as links to an RDBMS for storing non-coordinate attribute data.

A fundamental theoretical framework has developed over the past 15 years or so that can serve as a robust basis for moving forward—the notion of the discrete versus the continuous view. These can be briefly defined as follows.

In the *discrete view*, or entity-based view, distinct entities, such as a lake, a road, or a parcel of land are the basis of the representation. Their spatial and temporal extents are denoted as attributes attached to these entities. Vector models fall within this category. In the *continuous view*, or field-based view, the basis of the representation is space and/or time. Individual objects are denoted as attributes attached to a given location in space and time. Using land ownership information as an example, the particular parcel number would be an attribute of the entire space it occupies, with locations denoted in some continuous coordinate field. Raster grids fall within this type of view.

For both discrete and continuous views, there may by attributes that are either absolute in nature (e.g., a lake may have associated with it measured values of specific pollutants, etc.), or relative in nature (e.g., entities adjacent to the lake), or both.

Object-oriented data modeling techniques seem particularly well-suited for specific implementations of this representational framework.

Although visual analytics can capitalize on the wealth of existing research, additional work is needed to address aspects of geospatial representation that are central to the homeland security challenge. Work is needed to address the representation of uncertainty in geospatial information, to address the challenges of information analysis at multiple resolutions, and to develop methods that permit integrated analysis of both geospatial and temporal aspects of data.

Temporal Characteristics of Data

Some phenomena can only be sensed through time. Seismic activity and sound are examples of numeric data that must have a temporal component to be of analytic value. Other non-numeric data, such as video, transportation data, and textual news reports, also have a temporal aspect. When an event generates the data as opposed to an object in stasis, then time must also be measured and associated with the data points or the sampling rates must be set.

The presence of a temporal component changes the types of analysis that may be done and consequently affects the data representation as well. Data must be stored in a structure that preserves metadata about the temporal characteristic of the data. It must also facilitate transformations that permit examination of data in temporal sequence, aggregation of data along temporal lines, and temporal alignment of data.

Just as discrete and continuous views can be applied to geospatial data, they can be applied to temporal data as well. A discrete view can be applied to entities in space-time (dynamic entities) or to events. Examples of purely temporal events would be a bankruptcy or an election. Events that occur in space and time would include an earthquake or a storm. Whether the temporal (or spatial) extent of any object is a point or some interval is dependent upon the temporal (or spatial) scale being used to record the data.

Data may have multiple temporal attributes. For example, a news story has multiple times associated with it: the time of the event it describes, the time at which it was written, and the time at which it was distributed. Any one of these times may be important, depending on the analytical need. When temporal attributes of data are represented explicitly, they can be harnessed to support analysis. However, further research is needed to be able to reliably extract and exploit temporal features that are embedded in unstructured data such as narrative text.

Data Representation Research Needs

Research in data representations is needed to improve our capabilities to fully characterize massive data volumes efficiently and enable effective visual representations.

Recommendation 4.1

Advance the science of data representation to create representations that faithfully preserve the information and knowledge content of the original data.

Among the major breakthroughs needed are:

- Automatic or semi-automatic approaches for identifying content of imagery and video data
- Improved approaches for extracting semantic content from unstructured language data
- Approaches for consistent representation of mixed data-type collections
- Representation of complex space-time relationships within data at multiple levels of resolution
- Representation of dynamic data collections in ways that facilitate real-time analysis and discovery processes.

Textual Data Transformations

The key to making a difference in transforming incoming textual data for visualization is determining the semantic units for the data and visualization method that will improve the analysis in speed, coverage, and/or accuracy. This key is essential even in the use of structured and semi-structured linguistic data, such as databases and tables, where the semantic units may seem to be preset.

This section describes a few representative examples of approaches to textual data transformation, including both statistical and linguistically based methods. An exhaustive survey is beyond the scope of this chapter.

Vector-Based Approaches

Among the widely used statistically based approaches to text transformation are vector-based approaches. In this class of approaches, the content of each document is represented in the form of a vector representing its content. There are many good examples of vector-based approaches. Here, we discuss three of them for illustration.

Latent Semantic Indexing

One example is Latent Semantic Indexing (LSI) [Deerwester, 1990]. LSI looks at patterns of word distribution, specifically, word co-occurrence, across a set of documents.

Natural language is full of redundancies, and not every word that appears in a document carries content. Articles such as "the" and "a" are obvious examples of words that do not carry content. These words are called *stop-words* and are ignored in LSI and other vector-based approaches. LSI condenses documents into sets of content-bearing words that are used to index the collection. A matrix of terms and documents is created using these content-bearing words. The value placed in a cell corresponding to document d and term t is some measure of the importance of term t in document d. There are several alternative approaches for calculating this measure of importance, ranging from simple binary approaches indicating the presence or absence of a term, to counts of word frequency, to derived measures. The resulting matrix is transformed using singular value decomposition (SVD) [Forsythe et al., 1997] to create a more compact representation of document content. This compact representation can support document grouping and retrieval based on content rather than on keywords.

System for Information Discovery

System for Information Discovery (SID) is an example of a statistically based system for computing high-dimensional knowledge vector representations. Developed at the Pacific Northwest National Laboratory, SID characterizes natural language documents as vector-based knowledge representations so that they may be organized, related, navigated, and retrieved based on content similarity. SID autonomously identifies the working vocabulary of terms that best differentiate and describe a collection of text documents, defines a tangible anchoring vocabulary that is represented in a measurement matrix, determines weighted probability distributions for the working vocabulary in terms of these tangible anchors, and uses these results to construct an interpretable, high-dimensional vector representation of each document. The use of compact probability distributions and a tangible anchoring vocabulary allows interactive steering of representation based on user need for multiple points of view and specialized knowledge understanding frameworks. SID offers the advantages of scalability and speed of computation. It requires no training by the user, so it offers great flexibility. It supports processing of dynamic data sets and permits efficient incremental addition of documents to existing data sets.

Visualization systems can render interactive representations of document collections with an underlying vector knowledge representation by applying clustering, self-organizing maps, and dimensionality reduction techniques to form low-dimensional visualizations of the high-dimensional knowledge space. In IN-SPIRE™, the document vectors produced by SID are used to generate Galaxy and ThemeView™ visualizations. These visualizations allow users to rapidly understand the relationship between documents and themes throughout the document space [Hetzler & Turner, 2004].

MatchPlus

Still another example of a vector-based approach is that used by the MatchPlus system [Caid & Onig, 1997; Caid & Carleton, 2003]. This approach uses an adaptive neural network-based approach to creation of document vectors. Relationships among terms are calculated with reference to the given data set. Unlike LSI and SID, MatchPlus uses a training set. However, while LSI and SID treat each document as a "bag of words," MatchPlus considers the proximity of terms in a document, providing an increased sensitivity to uncovering the multiple meanings that a word can have within a document set. MatchPlus produces vector representations for words, documents, and clusters. This vector representation provides a structure that can be leveraged in the generation of visual representations of the type discussed in Chapter 3 [Caid & Onig, 1997; Caid & Carleton, 2003].

Probabilistic extensions to the vector space model approach

Several techniques are being developed that harness the combined power of vector space models and probability distribution approaches. A new class of research in generative models brings machine-learning techniques to the characterization of text data.

Probabilistic Latent Semantic Indexing (PLSI) [Hofmann, 1999] refines the LSI approach by grounding it in theoretical statistical foundations. It models topics as probabilistic combinations of terms; individual words are associated with a given topic. Blei et al. [2003] developed a generative probabilistic model known as latent Dirichlet allocation (LDA) to model documents as mixtures of topics. This topic-modeling approach has been further extended by Rosen-Zvi et al. [2004] to model both topic and author.

The Association Grounded Semantics (AGS) approach is based on the premise that an entity, such as a word or other object in an information space, is the totality of all that is associated with it. Using vector representations in combination with probability distributions, one can develop techniques for representing semantics and other aspects of meaning and knowing, such as unsupervised identification of entities (people, places, and other unsupervised activities) [Wang et al., 2005].

Natural Language Techniques

The techniques described above all derive their representation of a text collection without considering the semantic structure of the language. Natural language techniques offer a different approach that considers the text from a meaning-centered approach. These techniques offer a good complement to the "bag of words" approaches described above.

Named entity recognition (NER) and multi-word expression detection algorithms are improving and offer potential value in visual analytics. NER is the automated identification and categorization of proper names, while multi-word expression detection involves the automatic identification of multi-word phrases used to describe a single thing. Despite the results of public evaluations (see http://www.itl. nist.gov/iad/programs.html), NER is still not much more than 70% reliable on realistic data, even with extensive tuning by a computational linguist. This level could be inadequate for visual analytics if high recall—that is, the automatic identification of a high percentage of named entities present in the data—is critical to the analytic results. Techniques as simple as n-grams [Jurafsky & Martin, 2000], which involve examining sliding windows of *n* consecutive words, and as complex as full-fledged linguistic processing with co-reference resolution have been tried successfully for certain data sets under ideal conditions. Unsupervised learning has produced initial high-recall results above 80% with a handful of analyst examples. However, NER is not currently a solved problem for realistic, streaming data, let alone the volume of streaming data that must be analyzed rapidly and accurately in emergency situations.

Sense disambiguation, or the identification of the correct sense of meaning of a word in a particular context, currently relies on extensive lexical resources such as WordNet and EuroWordNet, but statistical methods show promise. Machine translation is only viable for data triage or the narrowing of a collection to the most promising sets of documents. A linguist must be called in to translate crucial materials. Topic detection, summarization, and question answering have been possible in English but work poorly across languages.

At this time, combinations of NLP techniques may quickly degrade the data because of the multiplicative nature of the error rates. More significantly, no normalization of names or co-references across documents has been successful enough to support visual analytics; analysts must still assist in completing the pre-processing or finding workarounds. As reasoning capabilities are visualized, the current understanding of negation [Polanyi & Zaenan, 2004], affect (that is, the emotional content of an expression) and attitude, and modals (auxiliary verbs that change the logic of a sentence and have abnormal time references) will need to be integrated into data representation for computational visualization.

Semi-structured data in tables with labeled rows and columns or other formats in written language have proven to be more difficult to interpret semantically than first thought. The data are often put in these special formats because of their semantic salience, so it is appropriate to find a data representation for semi-structured data that will support visual analytics. Semi-structured data have been worked on in speech recognition in the areas of air traffic control and air traffic information services. Hidden Markov modeling lends itself well to semi-structured speech data because of the relative simplicity of the language models required. However, it is unclear that the same techniques would work in cases where the structure of the semi-structured data is unknown ahead of the transmission. Work needs to be done to detect semi-structured data and to exploit their inherent semantics.

Unstructured linguistic data are the most common linguistic data. The nuances of communication through language can only be generated and interpreted by humans. Automatic multilingual NLP has been attempted for decades. However, to determine the semantic units useful for visualization and analysis, much research is still needed. Such research would support applications well beyond the needs of homeland security.

Intercultural Analysis

Culture has a significant effect on the appropriate interpretation of textual data. The incorporation of cultural considerations into data transformations has not been systematic. Successful prevention of terrorist activities and response in the event of a homeland security emergency could hinge on knowledge of the subcultures.

Theories in fields such as ethnography are emerging to provide experience-informed theories of how to understand and work across cultures. Hooker [2003] describes the dynamics of different cultures and theorizes that the best way to adapt to and be effective in another culture is to use that culture's mechanisms for stress management. These mechanisms are the dynamics of the culture for a reason and one must adapt them to become aware of and be assisted by the culture in managing the stress of acclimatization and everyday life.

The concepts used in Hooker's classifications of culture include relationship-based and rule-based cultures, shame-based versus guilt-based cultures, and polychronic (multi-tasking) versus monochronic (serial) cultures. These concepts are important to both the appropriate analytical interpretation of textual information and the communication of instructions to the community in the event of an emergency.

These culture-based concepts cannot be quickly identified or separated from incoming language data to make the language data culture-neutral. Instead, new methods of data transformation are needed that build upon ethnographic theories to identify and understand the dynamics of the cultures that are evident in the data and to appropriately reflect effects of cultural differences in analyses and models.

Text Transformation Research Needs

Much work has been done in the transformation of textual data for analysis, but the problem remains a difficult one. Technology advancements are necessary to advance the state of the art in statistically based representations. In addition, there are technology needs in all areas of NLP in dealing with unstructured, semi-structured, and structured linguistic data whether they come in as text, sounds, or images. Structured data perhaps require the least research. Normalization of names, locations, dates, and times within and across languages must be fully addressed if we are to equip the analyst to cope with multi-source information in circumstances ranging from emergency operations to long-range reporting to planners and policymakers.

Recommendation 4.2

Advance the state of the art for statistical transformation of textual data collections so that the resulting representations restructure the data into forms suitable for computer manipulation without compromising the information and knowledge content of that data.

Research is needed to develop new statistically grounded transformations that can support:

- Real-time characterization of documents as they are added to a dynamic collection. New approaches are needed that can handle massive data volumes in a computationally efficient manner.
- Multi-resolution characterization of document content. Techniques are necessary for characterizing documents at a finer level of detail than a "bag of words." Additional techniques are needed for characterizing documents at the sentence and paragraph level, and the section level, in addition to the overall document level.

Recommendation 4.3

Invest in the synergistic combinations of NLP and "bag of words" data transformation techniques to create higher-fidelity, more meaningful data representations.

Current successes in NLP and limits of "bag of words" approaches allow for synergistic combinations that have not yet been explored extensively. The combination of these techniques has the potential to dramatically transform the volume problem by maximizing the use of human cognitive channels through the presentation of only semantically salient data in normalized form. Integration of NER techniques, sense disambiguation algorithms, and multi-word phrase identification are all feasible augmentations of vector-based approaches.

Recommendation 4.4

Extend NLP to infuse visual analytics data representations with semantic richness.

The current state of the art of NLP is not adequate for the needs of visual analytics. Important research areas include:

- Pre-processing multilingual text, speech, and written or printed input
- Normalizing names, locations, dates, and times
- Using and developing intermediate representations from computational linguistics processing to support cognitive absorption
- Developing co-reference techniques to tie information from different languages, files, and databases to the correct topics, events, and entities
- Developing logical models of modals, negation, attitude, and affect to support reasoning.

Recommendation 4.5

Leverage work done in ethnography and computational linguistics to develop data transformations that can capture the cultural context inherent in textual data.

The need to incorporate culture within visual analytics systems is largely unaddressed today. This represents a significant challenge and a major opportunity for research.

Additional Approaches to Data Transformation

The challenge of data transformation is central to the success of visual analytics tools. Earlier, we outlined approaches for transformation of language data. While some of those approaches may be used for non-language data, they are most commonly used with textual data. Here, we consider more general data transformation approaches that are broadly applicable to a variety of data. These represent only a subset of the data transformation techniques that hold promise for visual analytics.

We describe three classes of data transformations: dimensionality reduction approaches that simplify data collections; discrete mathematics techniques that represent discrete objects through a combination of data and models; and modeling- and simulation-based approaches.

Dimensionality Reduction

Dimensionality reduction techniques provide generalized methods for data simplification. The ability to transform large, high-dimensional structured data sets into lower-dimensional representations is important for the generation of the visual representations.

Dimensionality reduction may be accomplished in two ways: by reducing the number of observations that must be managed or by reducing the number of variables that must be considered. Dimensionality reduction methods can be linear or nonlinear. The more straightforward linear methods identify global homogeneities to collapse while the more complex nonlinear methods search for local homogeneities.

For reduction of the number of variables, we consider two example techniques. Principal components analysis (PCA) is an example of a linear variable reduction technique in which new variables are produced by creating linear combinations of the original variables. A second approach to reduction of variables is automatic feature selection. The set of variables to be considered is identified through automated means such as statistical or machine-learning algorithms, or in simple cases they can be identified directly by users exercising their expert judgment.

Multi-Dimensional Scaling (MDS) techniques are an example of a well-established approach to dimensionality reduction. MDS techniques may be either linear or nonlinear. MDS techniques create smaller pseudovectors that approximate the high-dimensional structure of data in a lower-dimensionality representation that attempts to preserve the proximity characteristics of the high-dimensionality structure. Because there are many different ways to analyze proximity, and because of the nonlinear nature of the algorithm, it is difficult to interpret the results of this algorithm. One of the major challenges is to preserve the information and knowledge content of the original data set that was used to generate the original high-dimensional set. It is at least important to preserve the information and knowledge of interest to the visualization's user [Steyvers, 2002].

Newer, nonlinear techniques are also being pursued in the area of manifold learning for reducing the number of variables. An example is Tennebaum et al.'s [2000] Isometric Mapping (ISOMAP) procedure, which combines graph theoretic approaches and MDS methods to approximate the structure of the interpoint distance matrix in a lower-dimensional space. Roweis and Saul [2000] suggested Local Linear Embeddings (LLE). This method solves for the manifold using local linear patches. An alternate approach to the manifold learning problem is based on the eigenvalues/eigenvectors solutions that characterize the behavior of an operator on the manifold. Belkin and Niyogi [2003] and Lafon [2004] studied this problem from the context of a machine-learning problem.

Clustering of homogeneous data is a common method for reducing the number of observations to be managed. With large data sets, statistical sampling is often proposed as a means of obtaining computable data sets. The merit of the approach depends, to some extent, upon whether the task is to find subtle hidden evidence, in which case the information exists only in trace amounts that are unlikely to be discovered through sampling, or more widespread trends, in which case sampling is likely to suffice. There are challenges in producing random and stratified samples from databases and from streaming data. For example, there are numerous ways to pick half a million items from a billion items and it is non-trivial to guarantee that all possible combinations of one-half million have an equal chance of being selected. In general, it is much better to represent all data rather than to statistically sample the collection to reduce data volume.

Recursive partitioning methods are examples of nonlinear methods that can also be used to simplify data. These methods provide models that span categorical, ordered, and different kinds of numerical data. While not always obvious, many of the modern modeling methods developed in recent years are based on a combination of data partitioning followed by local parametric modeling.

Both established and new data structures have the potential to enable calculation of previously expensive statistics on large amounts of data [Moore, 2004]. The current trend is to use fast, cheap statistics to emulate more computationally expensive statistics. Applications include the fast calculation of likelihoods. Another current research topic is the scaling of algorithms to accommodate massive data volumes. New approaches take advantage of fast approximation methods to accomplish less important computations quickly, so that more of the computation time can be focused on tasks for which accuracy is more critical.

Another paradigm for analysis of large information spaces is to analyze the statistics of scattered data in very-high-dimensional (VHD) spaces, consisting of hundreds or thousands of variables. Sparse data also affect much lower-dimensional data sets, if the ratio of the number of observations to the number of dimensions being measured is small.

Analysis of sparse data is difficult for two reasons. First, the emptiness of these sparse spaces ("curse of dimensionality") [Bellman, 1961] makes it difficult to reliably establish neighborhood relationships. As noted in Chapter 3, interesting structures in these spaces may be non-planar (nonlinear), meaning that they cannot be represented easily in very low dimensions. Thus, analysis of sparse data requires more sophisticated tools than those used for linear analysis.

Fundamental developments in several fields suggest opportunities for new strategies and tools for sparse data. For instance, statisticians have found that the curse of dimensionality is not as dire as the theory predicts [Scott, 1992] and that many naturally occurring data sets fall on low-dimensional manifolds within VHD spaces. Newer, better tools in nonparametric density estimation, based on information theory, promise to be a good foundation for exploring such data [Haykin, 2000]. Another area of development is in computational topology, where researchers have proposed new methods for robustly parameterizing such manifolds and characterizing their structure, dimensionality, and topology.

Discrete Mathematics

Whereas continuous objects can be characterized by a formula, discrete objects are characterized by a method and require a mathematical model or abstraction [Maurer & Ralston, 2004]. These models or abstractions transform the data in ways that aid in analytical reasoning. Discrete mathematics provides mathematical models for a large number of discrete objects: induction, graphs, trees, counting methods, difference equations, discrete probabilities, algorithms, and n-order logics. Once discrete mathematical methods have provided the model, the data must be transformed into a form that fits the model.

One example of such a model is a semantic graph. A graph consists of entities as nodes and relationships as links. The entities and the relationships often have attributes associated with them in the graph. These entities may be extracted from the source data through a combination of semantic, statistical, and mathematical techniques. A relational data model is normally used as the representation for a graph.

A semantic graph is a type of graph that encodes semantic meaning about entities and relationships. Examples include relationships between people, places, and events. The transformations that produce a semantic graph are generally natural-language-based and, as discussed previously, are not without error. Consequently, measures of data integrity must be represented if analytics is to be served. Other government programs dealing with knowledge representation and data filtering have created sophisticated approaches to such noisy data and will continue to provide technology to transform the graphs and provide probabilistic query functions. However, research is needed to address the challenge of creating meaningful visual representations for the voluminous, complex semantic graph structure.

Modeling and Simulation

Modeling and simulation are useful in gaining understanding of the interaction of large numbers of variables and a dynamic situation in which there are many possible outcomes. Modeling and simulation transform data into sophisticated representations that depict the evolution of a situation over time. These outputs can be challenging to analyze, but they offer rich insights into complex systems. Visual analytics provides distinct advantages for analyzing these outputs because it can help the analyst clearly understand the phenomena these outputs depict through a combination of visualization and analytical reasoning tools.

Many modeling and simulation techniques are relevant to visual analytics. We consider agent-based modeling, neural networks, and genetic algorithms as examples here.

An agent-based model is a specific, individual-based computational model for computer simulation extensively related to themes in complex systems, emergence, computational sociology, multi-agent systems, and evolutionary programming. The idea is to construct the computational devices, known as *agents*, with some properties, and then simulate them in parallel to model the real phenomena. Because of the interactions that take place over time, new patterns and properties emerge [Axelrod, 1997].

A neural network is a processing device, either an algorithm or actual hardware, whose design was inspired by computer simulation of the design and functioning of human brains and components thereof. An artificial neural network (ANN) is a network of usually simple processors, units, or neurons. The units may have local memory and are tied together by unidirectional communication connections, which carry numeric data. The units operate only on their local data and on the inputs they receive via the connections. Most neural networks have some sort of training rule whereby the weights of connections are adjusted based on presented patterns. In other words, neural networks learn from examples, just as the brain learns to recognize things from examples, and exhibit some structural capability for generalization.

Neurons are often elementary nonlinear processors. Another feature of ANNs that distinguishes them from other computing devices is a high degree of interconnection that allows a high degree of parallelism. Further, there is no idle memory containing data and programs, but rather each neuron is pre-programmed and continuously active [Fausett, 1994].

Genetic algorithms use simple representations (bit strings) to encode complex structures and simple transformations to improve those structures [Davis, 1987; Holland, 1975]. The transformations are inspired by the computer simulation of natural genetics to evolve a population of bit strings in a way analogous to the way populations of animals evolve. Genetic algorithms have many of the characteristics of neural networks, in that they are parallel and can learn from examples to detect extremely complex patterns. Genetic algorithms are also the basis of evolutionary programming mentioned earlier.

These and other modeling and simulation techniques transform data into new representations that offer the opportunity for insight into complex situations. We need to conduct research to identify the additional transformations and representations necessary to effectively present this information to analysts for understanding and action in urgent situations.

Data Transformation Research Needs

Data transformation is central to the success of analysis of massive and dynamic data sets. The visual analytics community must stay abreast of the advancements being made by the thriving research community that is already addressing many of these topics. We must take advantage of new capabilities as they are discovered.

There are a few areas of special interest to the visual analytics community that are of lesser focus in the data transformation community as a whole. The visual analytics community must help drive the development of new transformation methods in these areas.

Recommendation 4.6

Pursue research in data transformations that improve our understanding and reaction to new and unexpected situations.

Research is needed to develop data transformations that facilitate characterization of current situations through the real-time identification of relationships, categories, and classifications. Specifically, new transformations must be created to facilitate the dynamic identification of new and emerging events and situations that were not previously identified or anticipated. Techniques that rely on a priori knowledge or training sets for characterization must be augmented with approaches that recognize novelty or detect surprise. Multi-resolution techniques are needed to allow the detection of both broad, emerging characteristics and very subtle, trace-level characteristics.

Develop a theoretical basis to represent and transform discrete data sets of varying scale and complexity.

Continuous mathematical theory has been successfully applied to natural science and engineering. However, discrete mathematical techniques require an additional theoretical base, especially when applied to massive data. Existing techniques are ad hoc and often break down as the amount of input data increases. Huge gains appear to be possible in the scale of data for which routine analyses can be pragmatically accomplished.

Discrete mathematical models show real promise in addressing the challenges of analysis of massive and dynamic data sets. Visual analytics must support the transformation of these models and associated data into a form that can be visually represented for analysis.

Information Synthesis

The techniques described thus far in this chapter address the challenges of representing and transforming data that are all relatively homogeneous in form and format. Similarly, most current commercial tools and research techniques focus on the representation of the unique characteristics of static collections containing a single type of data. Consequently, many existing visual analytics systems are data-type-centric. That is, they focus on a particular type of data or, in some cases, provide separate but linked environments for analysis of different types of information, such as textual data, structured data, and geospatial data.

Information synthesis will extend beyond the current data-type-centric modes of analysis to permit the analyst to consider dynamic information of all types in a seamless environment. The user should not have to be concerned with, or restricted by, the original form or data type, but should instead be able to consider the relevant elements of the content of that data in concert with data of other types. We must eliminate the artificial analytical constraints imposed by data type so that we can aid the analyst in reaching deeper analytical insight. As with all data transformations, the resulting data representations must preserve, to the best degree possible, the information and knowledge content of the original data, but these representations must also integrate the information content across multiple data types and sources. By giving the analyst the ability to assemble facts and examine alternatives without imposing artificial barriers on data, information synthesis will help the analyst gain rich insights.

To achieve the desired information synthesis, data transformations must permit the combination of data of multiple types into integrated collections via unifying mathematical representations. Because of the dynamic nature of the data, we must develop techniques to identify and represent significant changes in data. Methods for coping with missing, sparse, and inconsistent data are important in all visual analytics data representations and transformations but take on special significance in synthesized information spaces where the heterogeneous nature of the data adds complexity to the analytical challenge. Furthermore, methods for preserving and representing data quality, pedigree, and uncertainty must also be considered in order to produce a more powerful, information-rich structure to support visual analytics. Each of these subjects is considered in more detail below.

Combining Multiple Sources

Synthesizing data across sources allows an analyst to form a semantic model. This, in turn, leads to discovery of previously unknown or unsuspected behavior. Because the data streams are so large, contain multiple data representations and transformations, and represent multiple domains, data synthesis provides techniques to facilitate the cognitive merge that may not take place otherwise. A person's visual channel alone cannot overcome the limitations of formulating a model or set of viable models. Data synthesis addresses both the quantitative and qualitative aspects of the task and helps the analyst identify what is interesting and what is not. Otherwise, an analyst would have to sort through a huge set of mappings and views in disparate data forms to be able to gain a similar level of understanding [Hetzler & Turner, 2004].

One example of rapidly evolving scientific endeavors that parallels the homeland security need for information synthesis is the analysis of genomics and proteomic data in bioinformatics. The field increasingly uses the exponentially growing body of metadata to provide both broader knowledge and more focused analysis of new quantitative data. The metadata include gene ontologies (GO), the mapping of genes to GO, measures of the mapping quality, and the corpora of abstracts, papers, and data related to the genes and gene products of interest. These metadata provide a structure for a global information space that lends context to support multi-type analysis [Gentleman, 2004].

Combining data of multiple sources and formats, also called multiple media, into a single data representation constitutes an important research challenge for visual analytics. We envision creation of cross-media representational techniques such as a modified use of the context vectors discussed above. In a cross-media analytical environment, the vectors themselves may represent data content and context in a universal information space. This universal information space is the product of multiple data types and multiple data sets. The vectors contain sub-vectors that contain common cross-media content and context, while other sub-vectors contain specific, within-media content and context. This combination of a unified information space and a data-type-specific representation allows for maximum flexibility so that data of all types may be analyzed together or within homogeneous collections as needed for a particular task.

Identifying Change

Common data transformation techniques are oriented toward transformation of a single data snapshot. However, data are dynamic, making the detection of change in data fundamental to analysis. Changes in monitored data are often good early warning signs about emerging events of interest, even if the change is only partly or poorly understood. The quantity, variety, and complexity of data relevant to homeland security require novel approaches to change detection.

Change detection arose from research in industrial quality control during the 1950s. Today, change detection is used in a variety of applications, including machinery diagnostics, computer network failure detection, authorship change detection in text documents, and scene change detection in video. A common viewpoint in change detection is to consider a sequence of random measurements that are to be monitored for a possible change. The goal is to discover a specific time such that a sequence of measurements before that time differs statistically from a sequence of measurements after that time. The objective is to find the first such time while minimizing the rate of false positives.

A basic algorithm for change detection is the cumulative sum, or CUSUM, algorithm. CUSUM monitors a recursively defined quantity defined from the set of measurements and represents the log-odds ratio that any specific measurement is a post-change measurement [Poor, 2004]. Over the past couple of decades, a number of approaches for change detection have been developed that extend the CUSUM algorithm in different ways.

However, detecting change within homeland security data sources is more complex than the original industrial quality-control applications. First, the much larger scale of the data and the multi-source, multi-type nature of the data demand new approaches. Furthermore, data in the homeland security context are driven by discrete events. As a result, new methods for change detection are needed.

Accommodating Incomplete, Uncertain, and Contradictory Data

It is important that data representations preserve all of the quality attributes of the original data that they represent. In the case of visual analytics, data are often incomplete, uncertain, and contradictory. The data representation and transformation techniques used in visual analytics must both accommodate these data characteristics and facilitate management of them in an analytical context.

In dealing with the uncertainty associated with data, one must consider: 1) identification of uncertainty, which is frequently treated as a given but usually is actually well hidden and fuzzy, 2) representation of uncertainty, 3) aggregation of uncertainty, and 4) communication of uncertainties. Gaps, uncertainty, contradiction, and deception are characteristics of homeland security data requiring special consideration. For example, the internet, as is the case with many data sources, is rife with misinformation [Mintz, 2002]. Providing some automatic assistance for identifying, or even hypothesizing, that information is missing or incorrect is of substantial benefit to analysts.

Information can be missing for a variety of reasons, ranging from failure to have an observer or instrument in place to obtain the information to the inability to retrieve the information in a sufficiently timely manner. Examples of contradictory information and misinformation are readily available in financial, political, and social settings. Missing, incorrect, and contradictory data are conditions that frequently occur in scientific and business data processing, and practitioners have several years' experience managing these conditions. Dasu and Johnson [2003], among others, comprehensively review data preparation, quality, and exploration issues. Pattern analysis for contradictory data is also explored in the literature [Leser & Freytag, 2004]. Intentional deception is not typically considered in these domains, although it does occur in situations such as competitive intelligence [Mintz, 2002]. There is general, established theory for addressing the missing data in specific domains (e.g., financial, political, and social settings) [Little & Rubin, 1987; Allison, 2002].

For the purposes of visual analytics, a different slant on these data conditions must be taken [Berkowitz & Goodman, 1989]. Analysts deal with a combination of known facts that can be verified with a high degree of confidence and data with known gaps and ambiguities. Problems arise because analysts are required to make a best estimate using available data. They bring forward assumptions to help drive their evaluations. This can result in disagreements among different analysts reviewing the same data.

Situations in which different hypotheses are strongly supported by facts and in which gap-filling assumptions drive different interpretations must be made known to those outside the analysis community. Information consumers and decision makers would like definitive answers, but often the best product contains areas of uncertainty, unclear meaning, and suspect origins. When estimates and evaluations are made, descriptive yet subjective terms, such as "highly likely" or "unlikely" appear. Confidence levels are affected by specific factors that Donald Rumsfeld recently (and Sherman Kent, earlier; see http://www.cia.gov/cia/publications/Kent_Papers/vol2no3.htm) referred to as "known unknowns" [Rumsfeld, 2002]—items known to be important, yet unable to be estimated with a sufficient level of confidence.

Deceptive data or disinformation is provided by adversaries to attempt to deceive or mislead analysts. Deception and disinformation can cause intelligence assessments to go awry, distort confidence levels in intelligence channels, and cause broad questioning of related assessments even to the level of creating discomfort about the overall quality of intelligence processes and products. The typical approach to detecting deception in information, other than by directly identifying it, is through examination of patterns of anomalies. This is a difficult process because of the enormous amounts of information that need to be processed.

Automated identification of cues used in deception in text-based communications is preliminary but promising [Zhou et al., 2003]. Current theory for dealing with contradictory information applies in a focused technical area, in which the pattern of missing information does not carry information about the underlying model or phenomena. This theory and methodology are typically applied in settings, such as surveys (product warranty information, opinion polls, etc.), in which a template for all the possible information is available. This technical approach does not apply here; however, the theory might provide some cues or approaches for this technical area. Additional, less mathematical, reference areas include information on internet hoaxes and library science perspectives on evaluating internet references and using peer reviews (e.g., Wikipedia, http://www.wikipedia.org/).

Two aspects of uncertainty representation must be considered. One is the representation of uncertainty attributes that are known or can be identified. The other aspect is the identification, representation, or propagation of the uncertainty attributes that are not necessarily known and quite likely not intuitively obvious to the user. In the transformation of data to support visual analytics, it is important to transform the original uncertainty attributes in a way that they can be presented within the visualization for exploitation by the user consciously or subconsciously. The uncertainty can be made available to the user's mental processing capabilities independent of the uncertainty attribute ever being specifically identified for processing by the relevant algorithm.

Confidence Assessment

To ensure the appropriate use and interpretation of data, confidence levels must be represented. This confidence has its origins in the value and uncertainties associated with the data or lack thereof, with the source of the data, in the analytical methods used in an assessment, and in the perceptual aspects of the end user of the assessment. The identification and communication of confidence values are not easy tasks. Therefore, it is important that transformation of the original data preserves all uncertainty attributes that influence the confidence assessment.

We need to facilitate both the assessment of confidence and its subsequent communication so that that the user can understand both the information being conveyed and the level of confidence that should be placed in that information.

Information Synthesis Research Needs

Information synthesis is central to the major goal of visual analytics. To achieve this vision, several important research objectives must be achieved.

Recommendation 4.8

Pursue mathematical and statistical research in the creation of data representations and transformations to permit unified representation of dynamic data of multiple types and sources.

These techniques are central to achieving the goal of information synthesis. These techniques must produce high-fidelity representations of the original data. The representations must be versatile enough to not only permit cross-media analysis but also allow for more detailed analysis of data-type-specific attributes in homogeneous collections.

We must identify transformations that combine different data representations into more meaningful supersets to improve an analyst's ability to comprehend complexity. Current transformations offer solutions for a single data type and rely on a user's ability to look at and integrate the separate data streams. Extracting common threads in a more automated fashion will allow an analyst to derive clear mental models of the situation.

We need to explore other areas of scientific endeavor in which multi-type data analysis is emerging as a challenge, such as the biological sciences, and consider opportunities to adapt methodologies.

Recommendation 4.9

Develop new approaches to identify changes in multi-source, multi-type, and massive data collections.

Change detection is essential to identifying emerging trends and events. In emergency situations, rapid change detection is central to effective response. Change-detection methods are required for novel structures, such as those arising from discrete events, graphs, or spatial-temporal representations.

Recommendation 4.10

Develop new methods and technologies for capturing and representing information quality and uncertainty.

Quality and uncertainty measures must be preserved throughout the data transformation process and must be represented in a form that will permit their incorporation into visual representations. Accurate understanding of uncertainties is essential to the analytical process.

Recommendation 4.11

Determine the applicability of confidence assessment in the identification, representation, aggregation, and communication of uncertainties in both the information and the analytical methods used in their assessment.

The focus should be on leveraging the visual and spatial ability of the human brain in dealing with uncertain dynamic information. Any assistance in assessing the confidence of an analysis is of direct benefit to an analyst.

Summary

Data representation and transformation provide the mathematical foundations for visual analytics. They are essential to the success of visual analytics approaches.

Advancing the state of the art in data representation and transformation will facilitate computer processing and communicating the information and knowledge content of large, complex, dynamic, and diverse data repositories. Crosscutting research in information and knowledge representation approaches and into methods for transformation of these representational sets is essential to provide the underlying structure to support visualization.

Analysts need a complete set of tools to help them understand massive amounts of data assembled from numerous sources. We strongly believe that the techniques and recommendations in this chapter will expand even further. It is much too early in the evolution of visual analytics to know what data representation and transformation techniques will work best in a given situation. We will explore individual techniques and document the results to build long-term selection guidelines that will be based on the value of particular transformation techniques.

Summary Recommendations

The following high-level recommendations summarize the detailed recommendations from this chapter. These represent the path forward for continued research and development to provide the data representations and transformations needed for use in generation of the visual forms necessary for visual analytics.

Recommendation

Develop both theory and practice for transforming data into new scalable representations that faithfully represent the content of the underlying data.

From the standpoint of the analyst, border guard, or first responder, information provides guidance, insight, and support for assessments and decisions. Our goal is to illuminate the potentially interesting content within the data so that users may discover important and unexpected information buried within massive volumes of data. Each type of data presents its own challenges for data representation and transformation. In most cases, data representations are not meant to replace the original data but to augment them by highlighting relevant nuggets of information to facilitate analysis.

We must develop mathematical transformations and representations that can scale to deal with vast amounts of data in a timely manner. These approaches must provide a high-fidelity representation of the true information content of the underlying data. They must support the need to analyze a problem at varying levels of abstraction and consider the same data from multiple viewpoints.

Data are dynamic and may be found in ever-growing collections or in streams that may never be stored. New representation methods are needed to accommodate the dynamic and sometimes transient nature of data. Transformation methods must include techniques to detect changes, anomalies, and emerging trends.

Methods exist at varying levels of maturity for transforming data. For example, there are a variety of methods for transforming the content of textual documents using either statistical or semantic approaches. Combining the strengths of these two approaches may greatly improve the results of the transformation.

Recommendation

Create methods to synthesize information of different types and from different sources into a unified data representation so that analysts, first responders, and border personnel may focus on the meaning of the data.

Complex analytical tasks require the user to bring together evidence from a variety of data types and sources, including text sources in multiple languages, audio, video, and sensor data. Today's analytical tools generally require that the user consider data of different types separately. However, users need to be able to understand the meaning of their information and to consider all the evidence together, without being restricted by the type of data that the evidence originally came in. Furthermore, they need to be able to consider their information at different levels of abstraction.

Synthesis is essential to the analysis process. While it is related to the concept of data fusion, it entails much more than placing information of different types on a map display. The analytical insight required to meet homeland security missions requires the integration of relationships, transactions, images, and video at the true meaning level. While spatial elements may be displayed on a map, the non-spatial information must be synthesized at the meaning level with that spatial information and presented to the user in a unified representation.

Recommendation

Develop methods and principles for representing data quality, reliability, and certainty measures throughout the data transformation and analysis process.

By nature, data are of varying quality, and most data have levels of uncertainty associated with them. Furthermore, the reliability of data may differ based on a number of factors, including the data source. As data are combined and transformed, the uncertainties may become magnified. These uncertainties may have profound effects on the analytical process and must be portrayed to users to inform their thinking. They will also make their own judgments of data quality, uncertainty, and reliability, based upon their expertise. These judgments must be captured and incorporated as well. Furthermore, in this environment of constant change, assessments of data quality or uncertainty may be called into question at any time based on the existence of new and conflicting information.

The complexity of this problem will require algorithmic advances to address the establishment and maintenance of uncertainty measures at varying levels of data abstraction.

References

Allison PD. 2002. *Missing Data*. SAGE Publications, Thousand Oaks, California.

Axelrod R. 1997. *The Complexity of Cooperation: Agent-Based Models of Competition and Collaboration*. Princeton University Press, Princeton, New Jersey.

Belkin M and P Niyogi. 2003. "Laplacian Eigenmaps for Dimensionality Reduction and Data Representation." *Neural Computation* 15(6):1373-1396.

Bell ET. 1965. *Men of Mathematics*. Simon and Schuster, New York.

Bellman R. 1961. *Adaptive Control Processes: A Guided Tour*. Princeton University Press, Princeton, New Jersey.

Berkowitz B and A Goodman. 1989. *Strategic Intelligence*. Princeton University Press, Princeton, New Jersey.

Blei DM, AY Ng, and MI Jordan. 2003. "Latent Dirichlet Allocation." *Journal of Machine Learning Research* 3:993-1022.

Braverman A. 2004. "Statistical Challenges in the Production and Analysis of Remote Sensing Earth Science Data at the Jet Propulsion Laboratory." In *Proceedings of the Statistical Analysis of Massive Data Streams Workshop*. National Academies Press, Washington, D.C.

Burrough PA and AU Frank. 1995. "Concepts and Paradigms in Spatial Information: Are Current Geographical Information Systems Truly Generic?" *International Journal of Geographical Information Systems* 9(2):101-116.

Caid R and JL Carleton. 2003. "Context Vector-Based Text Retrieval." A Fair Isaac White Paper available at http://www.fairisaac.com/NR/rdonlyres/635C0BCA-2226-4C17-AD07-FD25913B331B/0/contextvectorwhitepaper.pdf.

Caid W and P Onig. 1997. "System and Method of Context Vector Generation and Retrieval." U.S. Patent 5,619,709.

Dasu T and T Johnson. 2003. *Exploratory Data Mining and Data Cleaning*. Wiley-Interscience, New York.

Davis L. 1987. *Genetic Algorithms and Simulated Annealing*. Morgan Kaufmann, San Francisco.

Debevec PE. 1996. *Modeling and Rendering Architecture from Photographs*, Ph.D. Dissertation, University of California at Berkeley, Berkeley, California.

Deerwester S, S Dumais, T Landauer, G Furnas, and R Harshman. 1990. "Indexing by Latent Semantic Analysis." *Journal of the Society for Information Science* 41(6):391-407.

Fausett L. 1994. *Fundamentals of Neural Networks*. Prentice-Hall, Englewood Cliffs, New Jersey.

Forsythe GE, MA Malcolm, and CB Moler. 1977. "Least Squares and the Singular Value Decomposition." Chapter 9 in *Computer Methods for Mathematical Computations*. Prentice Hall, Englewood Cliffs, New Jersey.

Gentleman R. 2004. "Using GO For Statistical Analyses." In *Proceedings of the 16th COMPSTAT Conference*, pp. 171-180. J Antoch, ed., Physica Verlag, Heidelberg, Germany.

Glassner AS. 1995. *Principles of Digital Image Synthesis*. Morgan Kaufmann, San Francisco.

Haykin S. ed. 2000. Vols. 1 & 2. *Unsupervised Adaptive Filtering*. Wiley-Interscience, New York.

Hetzler E and A Turner. 2004. "Analysis Experience Using Information Visualization." *IEEE Computer Graphics and Applications* 24(5):22-26.

Hofmann T. 1999. "Probabilistic Latent Semantic Indexing." In *Proceedings of the Twenty-Second Annual SIGIR Conference on Research and Development Information Retrieval*, pp. 50-57. ACM Retrieval Press, New York.

Holland J. 1975. *Adaptation in Natural and Artificial Systems*. University of Michigan Press, Ann Arbor, Michigan.

Hooker J. 2003. *Working Across Cultures*. Stanford University Press, Stanford, California.

Ilgen M, J Sirosh, and W Chonghua. 2000. *Novel Self-Organizing Neural Network Methods for Semantically Accessing Unstructured, Multilingual, Multimedia Databases, Final Report*. DARPA Collaboration, Visualization, and Information Management Project: Multilingual and Multimedia Information Retrieval.

Jacobsen R. 2004. "Statistical Analysis of High Energy Physics Data." In *Proceedings of the Statistical Analysis of Massive Data Streams Workshop*. National Academies Press, Washington, D.C.

Jurafsky D and JH Martin. 2000. *Speech and Language Processing: An Introduction to Natural Language Processing, Computational Linguistics, and Speech Processing*. Prentice-Hall, Englewood Cliffs, New Jersey.

Johnson NF, Z Duric, and S Jajodia. 2001. *Information Hiding: Steganography and Watermarking – Attacks and Countermeasures*. Kluwer Academic, Boston.

Kasik DJ. 2004. "Strategies for Consistent Image Partitioning." *IEEE Multimedia* 11(1):32-41.

Lafon S. 2004. *Diffusion Maps and Geometric Harmonics*, Ph.D. dissertation, Yale University, New Haven, Connecticut.

Leser U and J Freytag. 2004. "Mining for Patterns in Contradictory Data." In *Proceedings of the 2004 International Workshop on Information Quality in Information Systems*. June 18, 2004, Paris, France. Available at http://www.informatik.uni-trier.de/%7Eley/db/conf/iqis/iqis2004.html.

Little RJ and DB Rubin. 1987. *Statistical Analysis with Missing Data*. John Wiley & Sons, New York.

Mark DM, C Freksa, SC Hirtle, R Lloyd, and B Tversky. 1999. "Cognitive Models of Geographical Space." *International Journal of Geographical Information Science* 13(8):747-774.

Maurer SB and A Ralston. 2004. *Discrete Algorithmic Mathematics*. AK Peters, LTD, Wellesley, Massachusetts.

Miller G. 1998. "Five Papers on WordNet." In *WordNet: An Electronic Lexical Database*, ed. C Fellbaum. MIT Press, Cambridge, Massachusetts.

Mintz AP. 2002. *Web of Deception: Misinformation on the Internet*. Cyberage Books, Medford, New Jersey.

Montague R. 1974. "The Proper Treatment of Quantification in Ordinary English." In *Formal Philosophy: Selected Papers of Richard Montague*, R Thomason, ed. Yale University Press, New Haven, Connecticut.

Moore A. 2004. "Kd-, R-, Ball-, and Ad- Trees: Scalable Massive Science Data Analysis." In *Proceedings Statistical Analysis of Massive Data Streams Workshop*. National Academies Press, Washington, D.C.

Peuquet DJ. 2002. *Representations of Space and Time*. The Guilford Press, New York.

Polanyi L and A Zaenan. 2004. "Contextual Lexical Valence Shifters." In *Proceedings of AAAI Spring Symposium on Exploring Attitude and Affect in Text: Theories and Applications*. Technical Report SS-04-07. AAAI Press, Menlo Park, California.

Robertson G, M Czerwinski, and J Churchill. 2005. "Visualization of Mappings Between Schemas." *Proceedings of CHI 2005*, pp. 431-439. ACM Press, New York.

Rosen-Zvi M, T Griffiths, M Steyvers, and P Smyth. 2004. "The Author-Topic Model for Authors and Documents." In *Proceedings of the 20th Conference on Uncertainty in Artificial Intelligence*, pp. 487-494. Banff, Canada.

Roweis, S and L Saul. 2000. "Nonlinear Dimensionality Reduction by Locally Linear Embedding." *Science* 290(5500):2323-2326.

Rumsfeld D. 2002. "Secretary Rumsfeld Press Conference at NATO Headquarters, Brussels, Belgium." Accessed April 28, 2005 at http://www.defenselink.mil/transcripts/2002/t06062002_t0606sd.html.

Salton G. 1968. *Automatic Information Organization and Retrieval*. McGraw-Hill, New York.

Salton G, A Wong, and C Yang. 1975. "A Vector Space Model for Automatic Indexing." *Communications of the ACM* 18(11):613-620. ACM Press, New York.

Scott DW. 1992. *Multivariate Density Estimation*. Wiley-Interscience, New York.

Steyvers M. 2002. "Multi-Dimensional Scaling." In *Encyclopedia of Cognitive Science*. Nature Publishing Group, London.

Tenenbaum, JB, V de Silva, and JC Langford. 2000. "A Global Geometric Framework for Nonlinear Dimensionality Reduction." *Science* 290(5500):2319-2323.

Wang Z, E Chow, and R Rohwer. 2005. "Experiments with Grounding Spaces, Pseudo-counts, and Divergence Formulas in Association-Grounded Semantics." In *Proceedings of the 2005 Conference on Intelligence Analysis*. Available at https://analysis.mitre.org/proceedings/Final_Papers_Files/13_Camera_Ready_Paper.pdf.

Yuan M, D Mark, M Egenhofer, and D Peuquet. 2004. "Extensions to Geographic Representation: A Research Agenda for Geographic Information Science." In *Research Challenges in Geographic Information Science*, pp. 129-156, eds. R McMaster and L Usery. CRC Press, Boca Raton, Florida.

Zhou L, D Twitchell, T Qin, J Burgoon, and J Nunamaker. 2003. "An Exploratory Study into Deception Detection in Text-based Computer-Mediated Communication." In *Proceedings of 36th Hawaii International Conference on System Sciences*, January 6-9, 2003.

> *"Although we often hear that data speak for themselves,*
> *their voices can be soft and sly."*

—Frederick Mosteller, Stephen E. Fienberg, and Robert E.R. Rourke,
Beginning Statistics with Data Analysis, 1983

Production, Presentation, and Dissemination

Production, presentation, and dissemination of results are often the most time-consuming part of analysis. Too often, technologists overlook this step in the analytical process, but it is the only part of the process that is visible to the consumers of analysis. In emergency situations or in day-to-day activities, technology could make a large improvement in this part of analysis. Our goal is to bring creative research and development (R&D) efforts to bear so we can greatly reduce the time it takes for analytical results to be shared with their audiences, while dramatically improving the effectiveness of this communication.

Introduction

According to the *American Heritage Dictionary of the English Language* [Pickett, 2000], *production* is "the creation of value or wealth by producing goods and services" or, simply, "the act or process of producing." *Presentation* is "something that is set forth for an audience" or "the process of offering for consideration or display." *Dissemination* is "the spreading or scattering widely, as in sowing seed."

In the visual analytics context, production is the creation of materials that summarize the results of an analytical effort. Presentation is the packaging of those materials in a way that helps an audience understand the analytical results in context and using terms that are meaningful to them. Dissemination is the process of sharing that information with the intended audience.

The goal of production, presentation, and dissemination is to convey analytical results in meaningful ways to a wide variety of audiences, including peers, decision makers, and first responders. In addition, communication with the public plays an important part in homeland security. Although members of the public are not direct consumers of analysis, our goal is to facilitate effective communication of relevant analytical results to the public wherever possible. The highly successful AMBER Alert program for engaging the public in finding missing children is a demonstration of the dissemination of information to a broad public audience for their action. This program is a model case for an all-alert system whereby information can be provided to the public and people can, in turn, provide critical information when appropriate. Communication of the alert message to a broad audience requires a methodology and supporting technology much like what is being discussed here for communication among government team members.

Vision for the Future

Our vision is to integrate production, presentation, and dissemination seamlessly with visualization and analysis, computation, and data acquisition. Access to shared knowledge will be managed automatically to ensure security, privacy, and relevancy to the consumer. This knowledge will be dynamic. The consumer can add knowledge in response to the analytic results or requests for specific data. The analysts also will constantly modify the knowledge as data arrive and are interpreted in context, achieving a more accurate understanding. The visual analytics system itself will detect changes in data already analyzed and show the effect of these changes on the analytical logic used. Analysts may be engaged in collaboration, and relevant telephone or offline conversations should be captured as feasible. Interdisciplinary analysis will be fully supported by the tools, and these tools will be fault-tolerant and capable of operating under hazardous conditions.

In an emergency, we envision the analysts as enablers of complex communications that are appropriate, persuasive, and productive of immediate results. The analyst is adept at assessing data, while the audience for the assessment may not be. The presentation of analytic results needs to be clear and succinct, and it must take place as soon as possible after the analyst reaches a conclusion. To achieve this, we must equip the analyst to easily create displays that reveal what is going on, both in day-to-day analytical activity and in the heat of an emergency.

Tools will allow analytic reasoning, note-taking, production, presentation, and dissemination to occur simultaneously. Even for long-range analysis to support planning or policymaking, it is important to provide the analyst with the capability to build product during the course of the analysis with reasonable ease and be able to share the visualizations and associated analytical reasoning that led to the resulting conclusions. These tools will provide both rhetorical and graphic design support to help avoid potential misuses of presentation software [Tufte, 2003] that would obscure the message. Furthermore, these multimedia tools will accommodate the sophisticated communication skills of the analyst. Tools will facilitate communication with a variety of people who have different needs and objectives and who often use different terminology to talk about similar subjects.

This vision requires both a new culture of analysis and the incorporation of design concepts in presentation tools. *The 9/11 Commission Report* [National Commission on Terrorist Attacks, 2004] points out the difficulties of making adequate information systems part of everyday use in counterterrorism activities. Although there is an awareness of the need for sharing information, cultural change is slow and must be steadfastly fostered at every opportunity. R&D can make the vision reality, but administrators and policymakers, marketers, public relations personnel, and educators must see to its adoption.

State of the Art

Although significant research is required to achieve this vision, a few systems have made great strides in integrating production, presentation, and dissemination with the rest of the analytical process. One example is the Command Post of the Future (CPOF) system developed by MAYA Viz in partnership with military expert Gen. Keith Holcomb, US Marine Corps (Retired), and private companies Global Information and Telecommunications Institute (GITI), the Institute for Defense Analyses, ISX Corp., Oculus Info Inc., and Polexis. This system is currently in day-to-day use by soldiers of the Army's 1st Cavalry Division to provide security in Baghdad. As shown in Figure 5.1, CPOF "...allows commanders from battalion level and higher to feed real-time situational awareness into the system and have that information available in text and graphic representation immediately by fellow commanders and operations officers at all levels" [Rhem, 2004]. Soldiers share on-the-ground assessments by populating their maps with both hard data and partly formed hypotheses, bypassing the need for lengthy reports and presentations and saving the lives of soldiers who would otherwise need to meet regularly at a certain place to receive the presentations. The mission is also more effectively carried out because of the constant real-time sharing of each soldier's work.

Figure 5.1. *The Command Post of the Future system shows soldiers real-time situational awareness information using a combination of graphical and textual displays.*

Another example is Oculus Info Inc.'s Sandbox system. The Sandbox, shown in Figure 5.2, allows the analyst to organize and work with evidence from multiple perspectives simultaneously [Wright, 2005; Jonker, 2005]. Oculus calls the cognitive space where analysts see and interact with information *nSpace*. nSpace includes both the Sandbox and a number of components for rapid information scanning and assessment.

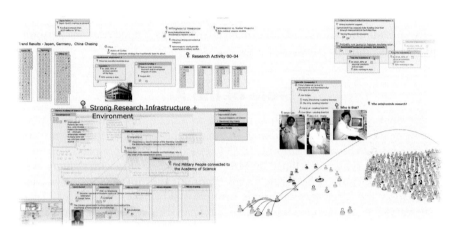

©2004 Oculus Info Inc.

Figure 5.2. *The Sandbox supports evidence organization from multiple perspectives.*

The Sandbox is a flexible and expressive thinking environment focused on human interaction with information. Manipulation and organization of information is direct and tactile. Analysts construct visible understandings with evidence and hypotheses, and then share them. The Sandbox creates a mixed-initiative environment for the whole analysis workflow as well as a workspace ready for collaboration. The visible thinking in nSpace is the cognitive corollary to the military battlefield.

In analytic practice, however, visually based analysis tools are generally entirely separate from presentation or reporting tools. Analysts can explore data and check competing hypotheses against data from a variety of sources using advanced visualization capabilities, examples of which were discussed in Chapter 3. For composing a presentation or product, they must leave their interactive visualization tools and move to Microsoft® PowerPoint®, for example, to portray their analytical thinking. An integration of analysis tools and reporting tools would improve the production process.

BAE Systems has been exploring the potential for integrating analytic tools with common productivity applications, such as Microsoft Office®, to support analysis. Their POLESTAR software includes a set of lightweight tools for structured argumentation that exist in the background of the analyst's familiar environment and are available for immediate use. These tools enable analysts to collect snippets of information from diverse sources simply by highlighting text. POLESTAR organizes snippets in a repository that analysts browse and search via an interface (Figure 5.3) similar to Microsoft Windows Explorer. This interface allows analysts to drag and drop snippets into Microsoft Word®, where POLESTAR then automatically inserts source citations, including all security metadata. Analysts can create argument structures either within Word or in an outlining tool (Figure 5.4) that enables the organization of snippets into argument structures comprising claims supported or rebutted by evidence. POLESTAR provides tools for assessing the quality of an argument, including a novel probabilistic measure of the degree to which the structure and content of the argument supports a decision about the claim. POLESTAR enables analysts to merge analysis and production into a seamless process that dramatically accelerates the formation of coherent arguments for or against particular courses of action.

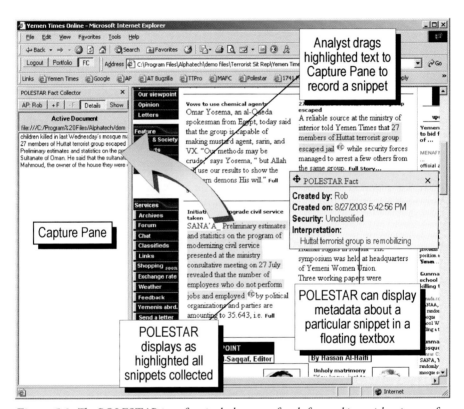

Figure 5.3. *The POLESTAR interface includes a set of tools for working with snippets of information to support structured argumentation.*

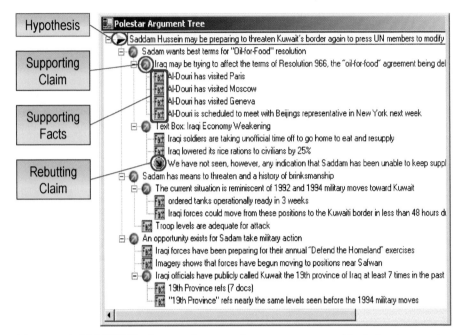

Figure 5.4. POLESTAR allows analysts to outline an argument and include relevant evidence, enabling the merging of analysis and production.

Technology Needs

To accomplish the seamless integration of analysis with production, presentation, and dissemination of results, research must be conducted to achieve several supporting goals: reduce the level of production and presentation necessary by enabling more real-time analytical collaboration; improve the quality of the products and presentations; integrate the creation of products and presentations into the analytical process; and provide guidance and support for the types of communication that must take place.

Recommendation 5.1

Create systems that provide shared real-time situational awareness to teams of analysts.

These real-time situational awareness environments must support sharing of both hard data as they arrive and hypotheses as they are formed and evaluated. Such a capability bypasses the need for lengthy reports and presentations. Although this capability has value in many analytical settings, it is especially valuable in emergency response situations. It gives emergency operations centers a radically better way to understand critical situations, coordinate their expertise, and manage their response [Tufte, 1997a].

In an emergency, the analyst's task is made more complex by the dynamic nature of the data and the unpredictable nature of the emergency itself. We must streamline the relationships among analytic tools, the analytic products, and the uses of those products to support emergency actions. As described in Chapter 2, emergency management and response are highly collaborative activities conducted under extreme time pressure. We must provide systems that allow team members to share their understanding of unfolding events and see what their colleagues are thinking via shareable visualizations that enable efficient collaboration with minimal time investment.

Valuable time will be saved as well if the variety of visual metaphors embodied in the tools provides cognitively efficient perception for the full range of data types. The military can use a map and icons as a basic display metaphor, but analysts may need additional visualizations that relate their reasoning and evidence, as elucidated in Chapter 2, or correspond to their particular area of expertise. The technology must robustly support collaboration, smooth operation across shift changes, and re-use of previous analytic processes and products.

Feedback from the consumers of analysis is critical for any ongoing analytic process. The many professionals who access and use the analytical products need to steer the analysis based on the questions and comments that arise in response to those products. Systems should provide electronic mechanisms for feedback that can affect the analysts' work in the emergency situation without disrupting their analytic activities.

In a rapidly unfolding situation, the analyst must effectively communicate needs for additional data. Current analytic tools assume that the data are complete and do not support a dialog for specifically requesting additional data. Technology is required to allow analysts to state when more data are needed as soon as they identify the need. The need should be transformed into a data request from the best source available at the time. The data should be incorporated into the visual analytics environment as soon as they arrive and the analysts should be notified of their presence.

Recommendation 5.2

Develop technologies that enable analysts to communicate what they know through use of appropriate visual metaphor and accepted principles of reasoning and graphic representation.

Principles for choosing appropriate visual metaphors must be completed. These principles, along with Tufte's dual principles of reasoning and graphical representation of analytic results [Tufte, 1997a; 1997b] must be made actionable in visual analytics software. Analysts operate under significant time pressure and lack formal training in the use of visual metaphor, so these tools must guide the process without constraining the analyst.

An informative example of the analysis and display of evidence is the Challenger O-ring incident, as presented by Tufte. "On the day of the launch of the Challenger, the rocket engineers needed a quick, smart *analysis* of evidence about the threat of cold to the O-rings as well as an effective *presentation* of evidence in order to convince NASA engineers not to launch" [Tufte, 1997a].

Thirteen charts were prepared to make the case, but the charts were unconvincing. The engineers correctly identified the O-ring failure at low temperatures, but the displays chosen to present the evidence did not adequately show the cause of the failure and overcome the bias of decision makers. Displays obscured the data, and the wrong decision to launch was made. The consequences were tragic. In an emergency situation, it will be even harder to make correct decisions. There will be complexities in the data, conflicting requirements, conditional analyses, and intense pressure. It is critical to address the difficult problems of communicating the analysis results to correctly inform the actions of others.

In *Visual Explanations* [1997b], Tufte lists the following dual principles of reasoning about evidence and the design of graphics:

"1. *Documenting* the sources and characteristics of the data

2. Insistently enforcing appropriate *comparisons*

3. Demonstrating mechanisms of *cause and effect*

4. Expressing those mechanisms *quantitatively*

5. Recognizing the inherently *multivariate* nature of analytic problems

6. Inspecting and evaluating *alternative explanations*."

The challenge is to ensure that products and presentations follow these principles. Presentation tools must be powerful enough to communicate different forms of the result for different audiences and analytic situations. They may need to present a single summary visual representation or an entire narrative story, complete with supporting evidence. Assembling a presentation may require pulling together the separate assessments done by multiple analysts. Part of successfully conveying information is explicitly presenting the multiple competing hypotheses that have been considered. Presentations may need to show both the hypotheses and the related evidence that supports or refutes them so that the audience can understand and evaluate the conclusions of the assessment in an informed manner.

Tools must allow multimedia composition with the ease of a word processor. They should facilitate the composition of a complete message, a persuasive argument, a sense of fidelity with the evidence, and collaborative and iterative composition. Composition tools must, at a minimum, contain rhetorical and graphics design support necessary to achieve the production, presentation, and dissemination of clear analytic assessments.

Recommendation 5.3

Create visual analytics data structures, intermediate representations, and outputs that support the seamless integration of tools so that data requests and acquisition, visual analysis, note-taking, presentation composition, and dissemination all take place within a cohesive environment that supports around-the-clock operation and provides robust privacy and security control.

The production and presentation process can be a natural complement to and extension of the analytical reasoning process. The hypotheses, evidence, and conclusions developed during the analysis become important components of the communication of results. By constructing tools that integrate analysis with production, presentation, and dissemination, we can streamline the reporting process and enable the analyst to spend more time doing the analysis.

We must develop standards for visual analytics data interfaces to support the requirements of advanced composition tools. The requirements for persistence of analytic product and presentation must be developed and documented, including tool input and output standards, data structures to support the variety of types of access to analytic results, and the hardware and software infrastructure needed to support emergency operations of the entire team.

Maintaining continuity during shift changes and emergencies can be supported by analytic technology. Visual analytics tools must include an effortless means of recording the results of analysis in a format that can be used during the next shift or in the next emergency. Being able to view and edit logical dependencies and uncertainties as evidence is collected is a critical part of analysis, but it can only be done if the data structures are shareable across teams.

Security and privacy are crosscutting needs. Laws regarding security and privacy of sources, data, and methods must be adhered to. Chapter 6 recommends specific actions to integrate privacy and security protections throughout visual analytics systems.

Recommendation 5.4

Write a handbook for communicating risks in emergency situations.

The book *Risk Communications* [Lundgren & McMakin, 2004] begins to address the problems of communications in emergency conditions. This book covers many aspects of communication, including visual representation of risk and technology-assisted communication. It also addresses communication in crisis situations by adapting the authors' more general techniques to potential emergency situations arising from terrorism or other intentional catastrophes.

The practice of risk communication documented by Lundgren and McMakin provides an important context for risk communications in general, but more work must be done to address emergency communications. We need to describe the members of the communications team and their roles in emergency operations. Best practices for emergency communication should also be identified and documented. These best practices will inform the production, presentation, and dissemination requirements that visual analytics software must meet.

Recommendation 5.5

Develop technologies that capture the results of an analysis, decision recommendations, and first responder actions into information packages that can be tailored for each intended receiver and situation and permit expansion to show supporting evidence as needed.

In an emergency, if only the analysts know the result of an assessment, that assessment has no effect on the emergency response. On the other hand, if the analyst manages all aspects of communicating the assessment, the analyst will not have the time or level of concentration needed to conduct analysis. Visual analytics tools and capabilities must have a straightforward means of packaging the results of analysis in a format that can be unwrapped for just-in-time use by other members of the response team without endangering security or privacy.

The results of an analysis must be communicated effectively to a multiple-level audience in an emergency. The communication will usually be through visual media. Advanced tools are available that take advantage of the visual bandwidth of the human brain to support analysis. The same advancement is needed in tools for supporting composition of presentations or products. The potential for communication far exceeds that addressed in any available presentation or production tools except for those that allow complete sharing of the workspace. The need to incorporate rhetorical and graphics design expertise in composition software will never be felt more than in homeland security.

It is important to make full use of visual approaches to ensure understanding of analytical results. Because of the gravity of emergency situations, tools must attempt to prevent human error at every opportunity and automatically provide an audit trail for review and training. Furthermore, differing audiences may be using different communications devices, so technologies must support clear communication regardless of the type of display device in use. We must develop presentation and production capabilities that ensure accurate, effective, and fast communication to all audiences ranging from first responders to the media to policymakers.

Summary

To be successful in revolutionizing the production, presentation, and dissemination of analytical results, we must incorporate R&D from multiple disciplines and sectors of the graphics industry. The automation of visual analytics naturally and necessarily leads to the incorporation of design and rhetoric into the composition of reports of analytic results. Multiple homeland security audiences and the immediacy of their needs for analytic results will spur the cooperation of visualization and graphic production developers as well as the development of rhetorical design capabilities within the workflow. The future holds the promise of immediate communication of well-analyzed results in emerging and emergency situations in the homeland.

Summary Recommendations

The following high-level recommendations summarize the detailed recommendations from this chapter. These actions are necessary to advance the capabilities for production, presentation, and dissemination.

Recommendation

Develop methodology and tools that enable the capture of the analytic assessment, decision recommendations, and first responder actions into information packages. These packages must be tailored for each intended receiver and situation and permit expansion to show supporting evidence as needed.

No matter what the end information product, the need to describe it, link it to its sources, describe its level of certainty, and put it into the context of the intended user is a time-consuming task. Few scientific methods or tool suites support creation of the end product. This is a high-priority area for near-term investments.

Recommendation

Develop technologies that enable analysts to communicate what they know through the use of appropriate visual metaphor and accepted principles of reasoning and graphic representation. Create techniques that enable effective use of limited, mobile forms of technologies to support situation assessment by first responders. Support the need for effective public alerts with the production of a basic handbook for common methods for communicating risks.

Emergency situations and the need for rapid, accurate communication for informed action by management, first responders, and the public bring to the forefront the need for analysts to effectively communicate what they know. Communications must facilitate teamwork that may include the public as current AMBER Alerts do. To motivate proper actions, the reasoning behind the results must be made as visible as the results themselves to decision makers.

Recommendation

Create visual analytics data structures, intermediate representations, and outputs that support seamless integration of tools so that data requests and acquisition, visual analysis, note-taking, presentation composition, and dissemination all take place within a cohesive environment that supports around-the-clock operation and provides robust privacy and security control.

The task of production can be accelerated and greatly enhanced in quality by a new science, methods, and tools to capture intermediate products of analysis, support mid-level assessments, and support note-taking directly within the analytical reasoning processes. This occurs across the span of information reporting requirements to Congress, to the President, and to the American public. The framework for this must take into account security and privacy policies.

References

Jonker D, W Wright, D Schroh, P Proulx, and B Cort. 2005. "Information Triage with TRIST." In *2005 International Conference on Intelligence Analysis*, May 2-4, McLean, Virginia (6 pp.). Available at https://analysis.mitre.org.

Lundgren R and A McMakin. 2004. *Risk Communications: A Handbook for Communicating Environmental, Safety, and Health Risks*. Third edition, Battelle Press, Columbus, Ohio.

National Commission on Terrorist Attacks. 2004. *The 9/11 Commission Report*. W.W. Norton and Company, Ltd., New York.

Pickett JP, ed. 2000. *American Heritage Dictionary of the English Language*. Fourth edition, Houghton Mifflin Company, Boston, Massachusetts.

Rhem KT. 2004. "Division Uses 'Command Post of Future.'" American Forces Press Service. Baghdad, Iraq, June 17, 2004 edition.

Tufte ER. 1997a. *Visual and Statistical Thinking: Displays of Evidence for Making Decisions*. Graphics Press, Cheshire, Connecticut.

Tufte ER. 1997b. *Visual Explanations: Images and Quantities, Evidence and Narrative*. Graphics Press, Cheshire, Connecticut.

Tufte ER. 2003. *The Cognitive Style of PowerPoint*. Graphics Press, Cheshire, Connecticut.

Wright, WD, D Schroh, P Proulx, B Cort, and D Jonker. 2005. "Advances in nSpace-The Sandbox for Analysis." Poster at Conference on Intelligence Analysis.

"A hundred objective measurements didn't sum the worth of a garden; only the delight of its users did that. Only the use made it mean something."

—Lois McMaster Bujold, *A Civil Campaign*, 2000

Moving Research into Practice

To truly leverage the successful research breakthroughs described in earlier chapters, these results must be moved into practice. They must be deployed and actively used to address homeland security challenges, or their development will not achieve its potential.

The process of moving promising research results into practice is time-consuming and often difficult. It is our goal to accelerate this process so that benefit can be realized from advancements in technology more rapidly. To facilitate this rapid adoption, we focus on four areas that have the potential to make or break the deployment of visual analytics technologies. First, new visual analytics tools, algorithms, and approaches must be evaluated at multiple stages in the research and development (R&D) process to ensure not only that they operate correctly but also that they represent significant advances over current practice. Second, issues of security and privacy must be addressed from the start and throughout the research, development, and deployment process. Third, visual analytics software must support interoperability to facilitate collaborative research, rapid evaluation, and smooth deployment. Visual analytics tools will be deployed in many different settings, often within existing architectures to which the tools must conform. Interoperability is one key to successful deployment. Finally, a concerted and sustained effort to insert the resulting technology into the user's work processes will be essential if the research results are to benefit the analysis process.

Within each of these areas, technology needs are identified; fulfilling these needs will enable or accelerate adoption of visual analytics tools and techniques. There is much research already being done in areas such as interoperability. Most of the needs identified in this chapter can be addressed via leveraging such best-in-class practices, although some may require new research.

Each section in this chapter develops recommendations via a survey of the technology, identification of barriers, and an analysis of the impact on the visual analytics agenda.

Evaluation Methodologies for Visual Analytics

The visual analytics R&D agenda is a very ambitious one. The research needs to address innovative methods for analyzing enormous, dynamic, and complex information, and the most promising technologies must be quickly transitioned into tools that can be demonstrated to improve the analyst work environment. When formally incorporated into research programs, evaluation has been shown to play a critical role in shaping the research and enabling rapid technology transition.

As new generations of visual analytics methods and tools are developed to support analysts, border personnel, and first responders, an evaluation infrastructure is needed to guide the research in promising directions. As with any new research area, it is often difficult to assess the effectiveness of the algorithms and tools. In visual analytics, this is especially true because a variety of approaches will be explored by researchers for different types of data, computation, representation, presentation, and analytical tasks. No one particular technique will be suitable for all problems. Further, it is difficult to assess effectiveness without realistic data, tasks, and objective measures, so it is quite costly for individual researchers to fully evaluate the effectiveness of their specific research. An evaluation infrastructure can supply guidance for experiments, data sets, test methodologies, and metrics and encourage collaboration and sharing of qualitative and quantitative results among researchers.

Benefits of Evaluation

The benefits of incorporating evaluation as part of a research program include:

- **Verifying research hypotheses**. This is a basic, individual researcher need. For many projects, other than purely exploratory research, it is important to clearly articulate the hypotheses so that they can be verified through some type of evaluation. Often this is done by an empirical evaluation if users are involved. For computationally focused research, this can involve performance evaluation on a standard data set.

- **Encouraging research and challenging researchers in a particular area**. Common data sets and evaluation metrics can help determine the most promising research approaches.

- **Increasing communication among academia, industry, and government**. This can be achieved by creating an open forum for discussion of research ideas, needs, and issues within an evaluation infrastructure.

- **Comparing technical approaches**. The goal is to identify which approaches work best in what contexts.

- **Determining if program goals have been achieved**. Research programs need to be able to show progress in identifying techniques that will improve real-world applications and thus must be able to clearly state how such progress can be measured.

Some issues can arise in a formal evaluation program. For example, once a test protocol, metrics, and measures are defined, researchers tend to design to the test. The danger here is that other approaches that show promise might not be pursued. Developing meaningful metrics is difficult—how do you know if you are measuring the dimensions that matter? When large test data sets are involved, it is difficult to obtain the "ground truth"—that is, the correct answers or outcomes against which to measure or to produce benchmarks. Finally, it is difficult to measure good performance of process. To measure user-centered performance, the performance of the user interacting with the tool needs to be evaluated. This requires instrumentation to capture the user interaction as well as developing measures that indicate good performance in the absence of knowledge about the "correct" analysis. Some of these problems are discussed in more detail below and, to some extent, in Grinstein et al. [2001] and Cowley et al. [2005]. To address these issues, it is critical that the researchers are part of the team that designs any evaluation framework.

Examples of Successful Evaluation Programs

A number of evaluation programs in related domains have been very successful in bringing research communities together, showing quantitative improvements and resulting in faster technology transition. Note that some of the examples are voluntary, research community efforts and are not part of any formal research program. These include:

- The Text REtrieval Conference (TREC) series [Voorhees & Harman, 2000], co-sponsored by the National Institute of Standards and Technology (NIST) and the Defense Advanced Research Projects Agency (DARPA), began in 1992 and continues today. TREC enabled the first large-scale information-retrieval evaluations and jump-started the text retrieval/search engine industry. Key to its success has been the infrastructure to develop a repository of large test document collections, test protocols, and relevance judgments for compiling documents relevant to test queries using a team of assessors and a judgment-pooling methodology. Recently TREC has also developed tests for the Advanced Research and Development Activity (ARDA) Advanced Question and Answering for Intelligence (AQUAINT) Program.

- The speech-recognition evaluation program [Pallett et al., 2000], also managed by NIST with DARPA funding, has been creating speech corpora and benchmark tests, primarily based on word-error rates, since 1988. The earlier work provided baselines against which researchers could then demonstrate the effectiveness of their recognition algorithms. Recent work has included the development of broadcast news transcription tasks to support the Topic Detection and Tracking research program and the Effective, Affordable, Reusable Speech-to-Text (EARS) program.

- The Message Understanding Conference (MUC) series [Chinchor & Hirschman, 1993] was started in 1987 for the purpose of qualitative evaluation of the state of the art in message understanding and has contributed to the development of improved linguistically based systems. Although MUC is similar to TREC, MUC focuses on the natural language research community while TREC focuses on the information retrieval community.

- The Knowledge Discovery and Data Mining (KDD) Cup (http://www.kdnuggets.com/datasets/kddcup.html) is an annual competition organized by the Association of Computing Machinery (ACM) Special Interest Group on KDD. Data sets and a set of tasks are created each year aimed at testing specific types of algorithms in the KDD domain. For the most part, the scoring of results has been straightforward. This is a voluntary effort not associated with a specific funded research effort.

- The InfoVis Contest (http://www.cs.umd.edu/hcil/InfovisRepository), which began in 2003 as part the Institute of Electrical and Electronics Engineers (IEEE) Symposium on Information Visualization (InfoVis), is attempting to create an Information Visualization Repository that contains resources to improve the evaluation of information visualization techniques and systems. This is also a voluntary research community effort.

Evaluation Approaches for Visual Analytics

Visual analytics systems are complex and require evaluation efforts targeted at different levels (Figure 6.1). One approach is to consider three levels: component, system, and work environment.

At the component level, analytic algorithms that do not entail user interaction can sometimes be evaluated with metrics that are easily observed or computed, such as speed, accuracy, or identification of limitations. Note, however, that there are some low-level component algorithm metrics, such as accuracy of vectorization, that cannot be computed.

Components that involve interaction require empirical user evaluation to determine the benefits of visual representations, interaction techniques, and overall designs. Metrics include effectiveness (e.g., time to complete simple tasks), efficiency (e.g., number of errors or incomplete tasks), and user satisfaction. These metrics are the standard ones for usability evaluation and can be applied at any stage of development of the component as well as at the system level. Limitations of visualizations can also be observed or computed with metrics, such as the number of objects that can be viewed or the branching factors supported. The interaction of the visualization tools with the analytical tools can affect the outcome, depending on those limitations.

Other research communities have been successful at promoting the development of tools and methodologies for measuring the effectiveness of information technology at the component level. For example, TREC [Voorhees & Harman, 2000] provides data sets and scoring methods, such as precision and recall, to evaluate retrieval methods. Those efforts are successful when clear metrics can be established to compare results of the tools with a trusted ground truth. The KDD Cup is also an example of benchmarking [Gehrke et al., 2004] where scores can be computed.

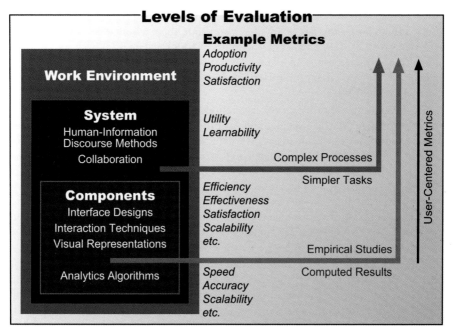

Figure 6.1. The three levels of evaluation and example metrics.

In the field of visualization, some limited techniques, such as described in Mackinlay [1986], allow computed scores to be generated to evaluate the potential quality of simple displays. However, controlled experiments with users remain the workhorse of evaluation. There have been demonstrations of faster task completion, reduced error rates, or increased user satisfaction measured in laboratory settings using some visualization components. These studies are particularly helpful for comparing isolated interaction techniques or data representations [Irani & Ware, 2003; Alonso et al., 1998]. Studies comparing slightly more complex tools combining components—for example, a choice of interaction and visual representation—are also available [Plaisant et al., 2002; Kobsa, 2004; Stasko, 2000]. These often reveal that different tools perform better for different types of tasks, but it can be difficult to identify what part of the system impacts the performance of the tool. Chen's meta-analysis of empirical evaluations of visualizations [Chen & Yu, 2000] begins to address standardization of methods to improve the clarity and comparability of visualization experiments.

At the system level, visual analytics combines and integrates multiple components, and the most fruitful approach to evaluation is comparing systems with the technology currently used by target users. Metrics need to address the learnability and utility of the system in addition to user satisfaction. Those evaluations often take place in the laboratory using surrogate scenarios but addressing complex tasks conducted over longer periods of time than component-level evaluations.

A new measurement approach is insight-based evaluation. The IEEE InfoVis 2003 and 2004 contests [Plaisant et al., 2004] have required contestants to report on insights gained over several months from the data sets. While these data sets are non-trivial in size, they are of smaller magnitude than required to evaluate visual analytics tools. The impact of contests is limited, but the data sets, tasks, and supplemental materials remain available in a benchmark repository after the contests. In addition to these contests, empirical studies measuring insight are also emerging [Saraiya et al., 2004].

At the work environment level, evaluation must address issues influencing technology adoption. Metrics can include adoption rate, trust, and productivity. Case studies and ethnographic studies are useful, but they remain rare in the field of information visualization and analytics. Case studies report on users in a natural environment doing real tasks [Gonzales & Kobsa, 2003; Trafton et al., 2000]. They can describe discoveries, collaborations among users, the frustrations of data cleansing, and the excitement of data exploration. They can report on frequency of use and benefits gained. The disadvantage is that such studies are very time-consuming and may not be easy to replicate or generalize to other application domains.

Diagnostic usability evaluation remains a cornerstone of user-centered design and usability engineering. It is not only of paramount importance for product engineering but also a powerful tool for researchers, because it provides feedback on problems encountered by users and guides designers toward better designs at all three levels of evaluation. However, as we have seen in this section, diagnostic usability evaluation alone cannot provide sufficient insight to guide visual analytics research in promising directions.

Finally, across all levels, it is critical to measure the benefit of the technology to the analyst in producing an improved product. This, by its nature, requires user-centered metrics. Development of such metrics for the analysis domain are in the early stages but do show some promise as described in Cowley [2005] and Steves [2005].

Challenges for Evaluating Visual Analytics

There are distinct challenges for the evaluation of visual analytics at all three levels. In particular, new metrics and evaluation methods must be developed for measuring benefit to the analyst.

At the component level, the main challenge is to move beyond the proliferation of isolated evaluations to a more concerted effort to generate guidelines for selecting techniques based on the tasks and data characteristics. A characteristic of the field of visual analytics is the great diversity of approaches available to designers to handle any type of data and the combinatorial explosion of possible implementations. Toolkits and code repositories will help researchers control some of that diversity to adequately compare individual components. In controlled studies, selection of metrics, data sets, and tasks has been an ad hoc process, making it difficult to compare results across studies. Studies would be aided by the development of comprehensive task taxonomies and benchmark repositories of data sets, tasks, and results.

Another problem is that studies generally include only simple tasks. For example, information visualization evaluation experiments usually include "locate" and "identify" tasks, but tasks requiring users to compare, associate, distinguish, rank, cluster, correlate, or categorize have been covered only rarely. Those studies are very difficult to design, and experimental design training for researchers would greatly improve the outcome of evaluation efforts. In traditional component-level empirical studies, users typically receive only limited training and are not allowed to consult with colleagues or use outside sources as they would in their normal work environments.

Another characteristic of visual analytics is that the analysis process is rarely an isolated, short-term process. Users might need to look at the same data from different perspectives over a long period of time. They also might want to formulate and answer questions they didn't anticipate having before looking at the visualization. This is in contrast with typical empirical studies that recruit subjects for a short time to work on imposed tasks. Finally, analytic discoveries can have a huge impact, but they do not occur routinely and are unlikely to be observed during a study. Insight-based studies as described in Saraiya [2004] are a first step, but new evaluation methods must be devised to address this issue.

At the system level, evaluation is a daunting challenge. Success is difficult to quantify and utility measures are elusive. System-level tasks are significantly more complex and difficult to emulate in a laboratory environment. Working with realistic data is crucial, but "ground truth" is not always available. Users' motivation and expertise greatly influence performance. Using domain experts will lead to more realistic results, but it is often difficult to gain access to domain experts for extended periods of time. Individual differences among users should be controlled for experimental results to be useful.

Discovery is seldom an instantaneous event but instead requires the study and manipulation of data repetitively from multiple perspectives and possibly using multiple tools. Facilitating the transfer of data between heterogeneous tools and tracking the history of the investigation might contribute as much to the discovery process as the individual analytical components themselves. Longitudinal studies may be helpful, but they are difficult to conduct. It remains a challenge to measure the impact of integrated components that require users to manipulate visual as well as textual representations, use the internet to find complementary information, integrate results of data exploration, and possibly spend hours brainstorming with colleagues to solve their problem.

Another challenge is that success may not be easily traceable back to the visualization or supporting analytic computations. For example, an effective visualization used daily by an analyst may heighten his or her awareness of certain activities by allowing the analyst to absorb and remember large amounts of information effortlessly. However, it might be difficult or impossible to link later decisions to a particular tool, because awareness is difficult to identify and measure, and decision making uses information from diverse sources. In fact, the introduction of visualization might even trigger changes in work practices, exacerbating the problem of identifying cause and effect.

Recommendations

We make three recommendations to support the critical role that evaluation will play in shaping the field of visual analytics.

Recommendation 6.1

All visual analytics research efforts must address the evaluation of their research results.

As we have discussed earlier, it is important for researchers to clearly define what they are trying to achieve and how they will measure their success. This will vary depending on the research project.

Recommendation 6.2

Create an infrastructure to support evaluation of visual analytics research and tools.

This evaluation infrastructure should include:

- An education component with resources describing experimental methods and guidance for running evaluations
- Sample data sets, tasks, scenarios, benchmarks, and metrics
- Access to analysts and analyst surrogates for testing
- Research to develop new metrics for measuring benefit to the analyst
- Research to develop new evaluation methods informed by evolving research directions.

Researchers must be involved from the beginning of the program to help define goals and strategies for the evaluation effort. The collection of baseline performance data is a non-trivial endeavor and requires researchers' participation.

The education component of this evaluation infrastructure must include important guidance for researchers in running evaluations. Human subject study requirements must be provided, as well as guidance on experimental design and analysis, statistical analysis of study results, and identification of appropriate users.

Research on the evaluation methodologies themselves is needed. For example, a framework and metrics are needed for evaluating visual analytics tools at different levels of granularity. One common task might be to determine the efficacy of different visualization techniques for exploring a data collection. A scoring metric would be required for this low-level, scientific type of evaluation. Another higher-level evaluation might be a "component-level" evaluation to examine usability attributes such as efficiency and effectiveness. This evaluation would involve identification of critical tasks and design of empirical studies and controls. Finally, to conduct a system-level evaluation of how a particular tool fits into an analysis process, we would have to develop and measure interoperability metrics as well as user-centered metrics, such as frequency of tool use and degree to which the tool is on the critical path to arriving at an assessment.

It will be useful to compile the results of evaluations so that past work can inform future experiments to be done on combinations of tools. For example, given a specific analytical tool, one might hypothesize that a new visualization tool or some combination of techniques would produce better results. A baseline for the analytical tool and the evaluation method would already exist, so it would be relatively easy to perform an experiment to test the hypothesis. In addition, if the performance of a set of tools under different conditions were known, an analyst would be able to choose the best tools for a specific type of analysis. One issue is that researchers seldom publish negative results, but for completeness we would hope to capture both positive and negative results.

Recommendation 6.3

Develop a knowledge base characterizing visual analytics capabilities based on the results of evaluations.

This knowledge base should capture the strengths, weaknesses, and limitations of visual analytics techniques. It should capture the performance of various combinations of interaction methods, visual representations, and display technologies when applied to different analytical methods and tasks.

Security and Privacy

The most innovative analytical tools can be ineffective or even harmful if implemented and deployed without regard to security and privacy considerations. To achieve the promise of the visual analytics research agenda, all activities must fully address the security and privacy implications of the technologies being developed or deployed.

As the scenarios in Chapter 1 illustrate, the security of data and information systems is essential to the successful analysis of emerging threats, protection of borders, and response in times of emergency. Analysts, border staff, and first responders must be able to rely on their computer systems to be available and functioning reliably in time-critical situations, and they must be able to trust that their data have been protected from any possibility of tampering from unauthorized sources.

Many types of information are needed to protect the country and respond in the event of attack. It is critical to be vigilant in protecting the privacy of any personally identifiable information to ensure that personal security is maintained along with the security of the nation.

Security and privacy considerations cannot be treated merely as a "wrapper" added after the fact to surround a tool or operational process but must be thoroughly integrated into the design of the analysis infrastructure. Consideration of security and privacy must flow through all aspects of the operational environment.

Furthermore, it must be acknowledged that regulations and standards for protecting security and privacy will vary over time. Integration of security and privacy technologies must be designed to adjust to changing requirements, while providing thorough enforcement of the policies currently in effect.

Security

Systems and information security, often referred to by the term *information assurance*, is defined as "measures that protect and defend information and information systems by ensuring their availability, integrity, authentication, confidentiality, and non-repudiation" [Committee on National Security Systems, 2003]. To this definition we can add "auditability"—we can neither learn from honest mistakes nor uncover deliberate system subversion when we lack the ability to trace back through the analytic workflow process.

Facets of information assurance

Below, we explore these aspects of information assurance with regard to the general analytic environment. These cannot be satisfied in isolation; each requires the others to be implemented successfully.

Availability. Although most often associated with defense against Denial of Service (DoS) attacks, availability addresses more broadly the issue of ensuring that the entire analytic workflow process not suffer from points of failure that may be inherent in the overall workflow design. In particular, no aspect of the analytic environment should be vulnerable to "overload" or blockage, either inadvertent or intentional, effected through the actions of any party or process to the workflow. Interference with delivery of analyst tasking, analyst access to data resources, availability of analytic support tools, and delivery of analytic work product each represent critical system throughput failures.

While good software design can help to avoid certain availability pitfalls (such as memory leaks and buffer overflows), there are also workflow design issues that can impact overall process availability. These considerations can be especially critical to the first responder, who will operate remotely and for whom bandwidth may be limited. For the remote operator in particular, vulnerabilities exist (e.g., many wireless protocols) that can represent avenues for inadvertent or hostile DoS interference.

Integrity. When critical decisions must ensue from the product of analytic effort, it is paramount that the information flows be stable and tamperproof. Systems designed to provide the analyst with a powerful environment for assessing critical information must provide commensurate protection against both inadvertent corruption and intentional manipulation to each aspect of the information-processing environment.

The issues of data and process integrity are critical to all security aspects but most centrally to authentication and auditability. For these areas in particular, technologies, such as secure hashes and digital signatures, should be implemented. (See relevant NIST Federal Information Processing Standards [FIPS] 180 and 186, below.)

Authentication and Access Control. If we are to ensure that supplied information is properly attributed and vetted, that subsequent analytic operations are attributed, and that work products are shared in a properly controlled and authorized fashion, we must authenticate all access to the analytic environment. Solid authentication is the foundation to access control. Especially in mobile venues involving portable, handheld access points in unsecured locations, biometric authentication should be explored. In general, the complexities of the analytic environment and varied need-to-know demand that role-based access control (RBAC) be implemented uniformly and produce audit trails. (For more information, see http://csrc.nist.gov/rbac/.)

Confidentiality. An analyst or emergency management professional tasked with making an accurate situation assessment needs clear access to all legally accessible facts. However, for others in different roles, access to the same data may be limited or prohibited entirely. The potential sensitivity of information, its aggregate importance, and the analyst's subsequent assessments demand that access be granted only upon established need-to-know provisions.

A breach of confidentiality in any part of the environment can be a critical point of failure. Unauthorized disclosure of an analyst's tasking, the nature of data retrieved, the forms of analysis conducted, or of the analyst's assessment can compromise critical operations.

While one expects access to information to be controlled according to a sound authentication and access-control scheme, there are other avenues by which information may be inadvertently or deliberately leaked. Care must be taken to avoid inadvertent leakage of operational activity through covert channels.

Non-Repudiation. Non-repudiation refers to the ability to ensure that an action taken by an individual cannot be later refuted by that individual or others. Effectively, non-repudiation acts to bind "evidence of action" to an individual. Such action might be to have been in possession of information, to have asserted a particular proposition, or to have issued a command. In certain contexts, digital signatures might be employed to this effect. Non-repudiation can be an important element of auditability.

Auditability. The ability to perform a retrospective examination of the analytic workflow is important to both security and sound business practice. Improvements in the ability to perform effective and timely analysis will be an ongoing effort, and many of these improvements cannot be made when the shortcomings of a process are held invisible to a retrospective review. Answers to questions such as, "What led to this decision?" "What analytic methodology was employed?" "What extra-evident assumptions were made?" "What information was under consideration (versus what information was available) at that time?" and "Who supplied or handled the supporting information flow?" must be made clearly available to those authorized for such access.

This level of thorough auditability presents additional and substantial challenges to confidentiality and privacy. Each analytic product should act as an "object" possessing all of the salient supporting information, to be revealed as authorized while remaining opaque to those unauthorized. It is possible that some combination of cryptography, anonymization, and "zero-knowledge" methods could be employed to address these issues effectively.

All analytic workflow access points and user-driven activities must be designed to support immutable audit trails.

Security regulations and standards

Security is an area of active research throughout government, industry, and academia. Security requirements for government computer systems are specified via federal regulations, and extensive research has been conducted to develop a variety of algorithms and standards for addressing these requirements. Table 6.1 lists examples of relevant security regulations and standards. The visual analytics research community will make use of the state-of-the-art techniques for providing systems and information security.

Table 6.1. *Examples of relevant security regulations and standards*

Regulations and guidance	
Federal Information Security Management Act of 2002 (FISMA) section 301	Describes federal requirements for security in developing systems for government information processing.
National Information Assurance Partnership (NIAP)	Provides guidance in meeting FISMA requirements.
Algorithms and standards	
NIST FIPS 180-2 Secure Hash Algorithm (SHA-1 through SHA-224)	Supports tamper-proof data and message integrity checking.
RSA Algorithms (RSA78 et al.)	Enables asymmetric (public key) systems, message encryption and sender authentication (digital signatures). See http://www.rsasecurity.com.
NIST FIPS 186 Digital Signature Standard (DSS)	Enables asymmetric-key cryptographic binding of possession or origination (digital signature) of documents and messages. See csrc.nist.gov/publications/fips/fips186-2/fips186-2-change1.pdf.
NIST FIPS 197 Advanced Encryption Standard (AES)	Specifies a symmetric-key cryptographic standard that can be used for electronic data encryption. (Supplants FIPS 46-3 DES as government standard for sensitive unclassified data, effective May 26, 2002.)
NIST FIPS 198 Keyed-Hash Message Authentication Code (HMAC)	Supports verification of the message integrity and sender authentication between parties sharing a secret (symmetrical) authentication key.
NIST Zero-Knowledge Password Proofs	Two parties can prove they know the same secret without revealing that secret in the process. See http://csrc.nist.gov/kba/Presentations/Day%202/Jablon-Methods%20for%20KBA.pdf.
The language "E" and the Lambda Calculus	A systems-design language supporting such constructs as secure electronic wallets and electronic contracts among mutually suspicious parties. See www.erights.org.

Recommendations

It is mandatory to provide the appropriate level of security within visual analytics applications. We recommend two specific actions to help ensure that security is addressed proactively.

Recommendation 6.4

Inform the visual analytics research community about security considerations.

Visual analytics applications present security challenges that may be unfamiliar to major segments of the research community. Awareness is the critical first step to ensuring that security considerations are appropriately addressed in visual analytics R&D work.

This education is, first and foremost, important to ensure that researchers do not disregard security considerations in the course of their research. Moreover, it helps facilitate the ultimate deployment of promising new technologies. Given the wide range of application areas for visual analytics research, a new technology may be applied in multiple ways in a wide variety of environments, ranging from the relatively unsecured public internet to highly secure, isolated systems. Each of these environments will place varying security demands on the application. When researchers have a basic understanding of the security considerations that their applications may have to address, they will be able to consider security issues during the course of their research and help position the technology for more successful deployment.

Recommendation 6.5

Use a common security framework to facilitate the transition of promising visual analytics research into practice.

Wherever possible, it is important to streamline the process of building security considerations into visual analytics applications through the use of a common security framework. This will help smooth the path to deployment of these technologies.

Privacy

The rights to privacy guaranteed to US persons are largely embodied in the First, Third, Fourth, and Ninth Amendments to the US Constitution (e.g., see [Griswold v. Connecticut, 1965]). Privacy is fundamental to our feelings of personal security. Moreover, reasonable guarantees to individual privacy are critical to the faithful exercise of democratic processes in a free society.

Protecting confidentiality and data integrity to ensure privacy and security is a key objective of the US Department of Homeland Security (DHS). "We will ensure the technologies employed sustain, and do not erode, privacy protections relating to the collection, use, and disclosure of personal information. We will eliminate inappropriate access to confidential data to preserve the privacy of Americans. We will maintain an appropriate balance between freedom and safety consistent with the values of our society" [DHS, 2004]. In their commitment to privacy, DHS has established a Privacy Office and a Chief Privacy Officer to carry out this mission.

The goal of visual analytics R&D is to create fundamentally new ways for people to understand and act upon the data available to them. However, this must be done within a framework that fully considers and supports the need for privacy in all phases of the work, from the earliest research stages to the deployment phase.

It is essential that privacy considerations be emphasized throughout the entire visual analytics R&D agenda. Privacy restrictions may even exist on data being used for research, and publication or other sharing of this data can violate privacy. To successfully address the needs of the visual analytics R&D agenda, all visual analytics researchers must be continually vigilant in understanding and adhering to privacy regulations and policies.

State of the art

Federal legislation establishes the rules for safeguarding privacy. Two pieces of legislation are particularly relevant:

- **Privacy Act of 1974 (Title 5 USC Sec 552a)** details the legal proscriptions to government maintenance of records on individuals. These proscriptions address conditions of disclosure, accounting of disclosures, access to records, agency requirements and rules, and general and specific exemptions. They specifically address "matching" agreements and reporting requirements for new systems and matching programs. See http://www.usdoj.gov/04foia/privstat.htm.
- **Federal Information Security Management Act of 2002 (FISMA)** governs the use of information garnered in "e-government" initiatives. Section 208 addresses specifically the relevant privacy considerations. For a helpful discussion of this law, see http://cio.doe.gov/Conferences/AITC/presentations/schlarman.ppt.

Additional guidance in protecting privacy rights appears in the Department of Defense Technology and Privacy Advisory Committee (TAPAC) report released in 2004 [Department of Defense TAPAC, 2004]. This report recommends use of several techniques in an effort to improve privacy:

- **Data minimization** – using the least possible data to accomplish a task
- **Data anonymization** – wherever possible, using data from which personal identification information has been removed
- **Audit trails** – maintaining permanent and unalterable records of access to information
- **Security constraints** – protecting computer systems to guard against unauthorized access
- **Training** – ensuring that everyone involved in development of new computer systems understands the rules regarding privacy protection and can ensure that their systems comply with those rules.

Several technologies have been developed to enhance privacy in computer systems:

- **Salted Hashing**. This technique enables privacy-safe correlation and matching of data from disparate data owners while resisting dictionary attacks on anonymized data [Dempsey & Rosenzweig, 2004].
- **Feature Perturbation in Pattern-Based Searches**. This technique uses randomized distortions in sensitive specifics of anonymized individuals to limit unauthorized matching and re-identification while preserving fidelity in cluster generation [Oliveira & Zaiane, 2003].

- **Hippocratic Databases**. These databases enforce principles such as ensuring that personal data are tagged for purpose and requiring queries for which purpose-based authorization mitigates access to privacy fields [Agrawal et al., 2002].

Technology needs

All processes for handling analytical inputs and outputs should be prepared to cope with and accommodate data that have been variably obscured or anonymized.

There are several opportunities for streamlining the implementation of robust privacy protection measures. For example, it is worthwhile to investigate the establishment of a standard independent privacy brokerage architecture. Data access and dissemination should proceed only through a uniform and independent data brokerage layer cognizant of privacy policies, capable of enforcing data anonymization mapping, and of releasing such mapping in conformance to policy and upon receipt of appropriate and secured need-to-know credentials.

Such a framework would provide a uniform interface for the array of analytic information processing needs, freeing individual groups from the burdens of hand-crafting privacy procedures, and facilitating inter-agency sharing of analytic products. Ideally, the framework could be placed under the control of an independent brokerage operation. Doing so would help to insulate the analytic operations environment from opportunities for abuse and enhance public confidence in the integrity of the analytic mission.

Another area for research advancement exists in the development of uniform anonymization services. There is also value to conducting research on the impact of data minimization and anonymization on the analytical process, with the goal of identifying the effect of these techniques on the analytic product and the degree of privacy protection afforded by various schemes. The results of this research will provide a basis for the design of new analytical systems and services.

Recommendations

It is essential that visual analytics tools adhere to privacy laws and policies in all phases of research, development, and deployment. We recommend two actions to help ensure that the appropriate privacy protections are provided.

Recommendation 6.6

Inform the visual analytics research community about privacy considerations and techniques for providing privacy protections in their software.

Techniques such as data anonymization and data minimization will be used to maintain privacy protections. It will be critical to educate the research community on the privacy considerations related to their research and build the awareness necessary so that privacy is a focus.

It is critical to build awareness in the research community about the sensitivities associated with personally identifiable data. Researchers must be made aware that even the exposure of test data can violate privacy regulations. Test data must be sufficiently anonymized or otherwise protected in order to guarantee privacy. Software must be able to accommodate the use of anonymized or minimized data.

Researchers must have a basic understanding of the privacy considerations that their applications may have to address, so that they can consider these issues throughout their R&D process.

Identify and share methods that strengthen the privacy protection, and move these best practices into a common set of services for data privacy protection.

There is much value to be gained from streamlining the process of implementing privacy protection measures. By creating common services that can be shared across the R&D community, the implementation effort associated with privacy protection can be minimized.

Interoperability

Interoperability is essential to the success of visual analytics tools. It also plays a critical role in helping to meet the goal of accelerating the transition of the most promising research tools into analytical use. Interoperability is the ability for different pieces of software written independently to work together. This ability is important to the visual analytics community at three different stages:

- In the research stages, code interoperability permits researchers to share software so that they can spend less time reinventing common functionality and more time addressing their central research questions.

- In the evaluation stages, prototypes must be bundled into complementary collections and evaluated in a common operational environment. Designing software prototypes with interoperability in mind will speed the evaluation process.

- As the most promising research is transitioned into practice, robust, production-quality software will be developed. It may be deployed in many different environments to meet varying analytical needs. As a result, it may need to interface with a wide variety of data repositories and other tools within the analyst's toolkit. Interoperability in an operational setting will be required if tools are to be adopted and used.

A significant body of computer science research is devoted to software architectures and interoperability approaches. The visual analytics community must stay aware of the advancements in this community and adopt new methods that offer opportunities for improved software interoperability and development efficiency.

As discussed in Chapter 3, the research community has developed some promising approaches to constructing visualization systems. These approaches should be kept in mind as we pursue strategies for interoperability.

Interoperability in the Research Environment

Interoperability, in the broadest sense, is a continuum of capability that ranges from informal discussions of ideas and algorithms to the sharing of software modules.

In our vision of research software interoperability, different developers, working almost entirely independently, can contribute software components to a common, quality-assured collection (e.g., a repository). These components can be easily obtained from this collection and combined into larger assemblies using a variety of interconnection mechanisms.

This vision addresses a number of factors that influence the successful sharing of software among developers. For example, the idea that developers can work almost entirely independently is crucial. The more human interaction that is needed to share and exchange software, the less likely it is to happen over a large number of developers such as the visual analytics community. The idea of a quality-assured collection is also critical. What good is it to a developer if the software that can be obtained through interoperating with other developers does not work or performs poorly? The idea that components can be easily obtained from a collection is another important factor. For a developer to use someone else's software, the developer must first know that it even exists. It is also important to be able to easily locate and obtain the actual software. There are other issues as well, such as defining the appropriate granularity of the software components to be shared. Are they code fragments, libraries, or whole executable programs? Another issue is the ease with which a component can be integrated into new software settings.

Today, no framework is in place to achieve the kind of research software interoperability we envision. More effort needs to be made to develop and leverage the best practices and standards to support interoperability. For example, at a basic level, we need the ability to access common data formats for many system components. Users of today's visual analytics systems usually have to convert their data to a specific format to try out a new or different software tool. Often, this conversion is a painstaking process. Today, there is no formal mechanism in place for the exchange of software except for joint projects. Without a formal mechanism, interoperability will be difficult.

Benefits of interoperability

Benefits of interoperability are easy to enumerate. Sharing code or code fragments will make development faster, avoid duplication of effort, and reduce the cost of development. New functionality will be easier to add and users will have a wider choice of capabilities to choose from. Analysts and researchers will better be able to explore alternative combinations of tools.

Users of visual analytics software will view interoperability differently than software developers. The user is interested in ease of use, consistency of the user interface, and user interface terminology that reflects the terminology used in his or her field of expertise. The developer may be more interested in portability issues, flexibility, and access to the source code. Both user and developer are interested in robustness, performance, functionality, and portability.

Most collaboration is done on an informal basis at conferences or meetings. Conferences such as ACM Computer-Human Interaction (CHI), ACM Special Interest Group on Graphical Displays (SIGGRAPH), and the IEEE Visualization conferences provide an opportunity for learning about current research in the fields of visualization, computer graphics, and interaction design. These conferences provide a forum for exchanging information, ideas, and algorithms, and they can help the participants focus their research by learning about complementary efforts by others. Although researchers' professional networks are valuable in identifying complementary or duplicative research efforts, a readily accessible and systematic approach to sharing information about research efforts would benefit the entire research community.

Challenges to interoperability

There are challenges to interoperability that must be overcome to create the envisioned research environment.

For a piece of research software to be shared, it must be tested and documented so that others outside the immediate team can use it appropriately, and there is a cost associated with this effort. Standards and best practices for software development should be followed to formalize these testing and documentation steps as a routine part of the research process.

Many technical barriers to interoperability must also be addressed. Support for massive data sets imposes efficiency considerations on software tools. The need to integrate diverse and dynamic data into a common visual analytic environment demands software versatility and flexibility. Given the user-centric nature of visual analytics systems, software must provide rapid and predictable response times on large data sets. Mechanisms for providing research interoperability must address the unique issues created by the scale of the analytic problem.

Interoperability approaches must support the need for remote collaboration. The locations of research computer servers and researchers are becoming more dispersed. Researchers may collaborate simultaneously with other researchers at different sites to visualize and interact with their data. Research interoperability approaches need to support this collaboration.

The benefits of research interoperability and collaboration must be made apparent to the researchers so that they are willing and motivated participants. Frequently, researchers are driven by the short-term needs of their scientific programs, and producing a software module that can be shared with others is not seen as a high priority by their management.

The issue of intellectual property rights must be addressed explicitly. The intellectual property rights of the software creator must be respected, and processes must be well understood for defining intellectual property ownership in the case of shared development.

To address these challenges will demand a practical approach that emphasizes sharing at a level that benefits the participants without limiting intellectual property rights of the inventors. Sharing of run-time versions of software that provide documented application programming interfaces (APIs) can benefit all researchers. The initial focus should be placed on sharing crosscutting modules that can alleviate some of the software infrastructure burden, such as the services for data anonymization discussed previously.

Interoperability Needs in Evaluation and Operation

System interoperability is critical, not only to support research but also to support its evaluation and transition into operation. Promising research results will be evaluated in concert to assess their effectiveness in supporting analytical goals. In this critical evaluation stage, complementary tools must work together with a minimum of complication to permit a fair evaluation of their potential. The most promising research results will mature into software applications that may be deployed in a wide variety of environments, requiring them to work seamlessly with data repositories of many different types and interface with other tools in the user's toolkit. Although they will be an important part of the analytic environment, visual analytics tools will not be able to control the broader architectures in which they must operate. Instead, visual analytics tools must work within the software architectures that have been established to meet the larger computing needs of the users' organizations.

As a result, there are a number of system interoperability challenges facing the visual analytics community.

Simplifying the interface between visual analytics software and other software tools. Visual analytics tools will often be used in conjunction with other tools, such as repository search and retrieval tools or productivity support tools, such as e-mail or word processing. Straightforward mechanisms must be developed to simplify the process of implementing interfaces to these and other tools.

Simultaneous analysis of data from multiple collections. Data from many different repositories must often be brought together in a single analytical environment to produce the needed insights. These differing data collections may be inconsistent in organization and terminology as well as access mechanism. A mechanism for reconciling these differences and simplifying the construction of interfaces to new repositories must be addressed to permit the needed analysis.

Supporting analysis of dynamic data. It is generally insufficient for an analytical tool to take a single snapshot of current data and use that over the course of an extended analysis, because new data may become available at any time to completely alter the outcome of the analysis. To sustain an analysis of dynamic data will require an active interface between the visual analytics tools and the underlying data repositories.

Analyzing very large data sets. Interoperability techniques that work well on small amounts of data may break down rapidly as the scale of the data set grows. The volumes of data transferred among applications may quickly become prohibitive. Interfaces among tools must be sensitive to the demands posed by analysis of very large data sets. We must investigate techniques that minimize the load posed by very large data sets, whether through adaptive level-of-detail and multi-resolution techniques, or discovery and filtering tools.

Balancing performance with interoperability. Analytical and emergency response applications generally demand high performance, which can be difficult to achieve in environments that offer a high degree of interoperability. If interoperability is achieved by implementing layers of virtual interfaces, the overhead associated with such layers is, in some cases, unacceptable.

Balancing the rate of change. Computational technologies (both hardware and software) are advancing rapidly. When a new technology becomes available, there is often increased pressure from the research community to exploit the new technology. However, operational environments will have their own varying timetables for adoption of new computational technologies. The more critical a computer system is operationally, the less likely it is that computing environments will be early adopters of new operating systems and computing platforms. As a result, visual analytics tools must be able to support interoperability in a wide variety of environments.

Supporting diverse application domains. As applications are deployed in diverse domains, visual analytics tools will need to adapt to the varying terminology and semantics associated with different application domains.

Accommodating these demands comes at a price. In addition to the costs of designing and building interoperable software, it must also be recognized that significant work is needed to make any research-grade software production-quality. A well-defined set of standards and best practices for software development should be followed to enhance and ensure the interoperability of the code being developed and simplify this transition from research into practice as much as possible.

Recommendations

Interoperability can be a deciding factor in whether or not a visual analytics capability is adopted for broad use. We recommend two actions that will help create a climate that supports interoperability in all phases of the research, development, and operation cycle.

Recommendation 6.8

Develop and share interchange standards and best software engineering principles and practices to facilitate interoperability.

A significant body of computer science research is devoted to software architectures and interoperability approaches. The visual analytics community must stay aware of the advancements in this community and adopt new methods that offer opportunities for improved software interoperability and development efficiency.

Recommendation 6.9

Develop software architectures that can be used, where practical, to facilitate interoperability, testing, evaluation, and deployment of algorithms, interaction and visualization tools, analytical tools, knowledge modeling tools, and other software components. The architectures must be flexible and must evolve over time to fit the changing needs of the visual analytics community.

Visual analytics tools will ultimately be deployed in numerous software architectures, the specifications of which are generally outside the control of the visual analytics tool developer. However, there is value to creating architectures as a means of achieving interoperability in situations where they can be used. Architecture development can support efforts to test and evaluate research prototypes, as well as selected software deployments in cases where external architectural constraints have not been applied.

Technology Insertion

Technology insertion is the point at which the promise of visual analytics research and development is actually realized in operation. Technology insertion is the process of delivering advanced information technologies in ways that enable users to apply them effectively. It is the set of steps necessary to bridge the gulf between promising research and the practical, day-to-day application of reliable and well-understood software programs.

It is important to accomplish the R&D agenda's end goal of inserting technologies into the diverse user community supporting the homeland security mission. Insertion of advanced information technologies is not easy and will not happen automatically. When it is planned into the R&D process, it can be very successful. However, this part of the process has not often received sufficient attention or has encountered organizational barriers. Historically, many promising research results have gone unused because the technology insertion infrastructure was not in place to support their deployment.

Successful technology insertion requires comprehensive planning and cooperation involving both government organizations and R&D teams. It can only be accomplished through an ongoing team effort, with active participation by scientists and engineers, R&D managers, information services infrastructure personnel, and user organizations.

Technology insertion is a corporate function and must be acknowledged, sponsored, and advocated at the highest level. The few successes in developing new information technology (IT) and inserting it into use have come from a larger corporate teaming of personnel with each individual participant coming to the team with a different set of needed skills as well as a high level of enthusiasm. To set the climate for systematic success in technology insertion, an advanced information technology insertion organization must exist at the highest level and must be separate from the information services infrastructure function. However, this organization must have a charter to work closely in a coordinated manner with the information services infrastructure organization.

Technology insertion is a multi-faceted process. It builds upon a fundamental understanding of user needs that is gained during the iterative research process. As the decision is made to transition the most promising research into operational systems, new partners must become involved in the process. Government organizations that sponsor research must become partners with the IT infrastructure organizations that have the intimate working knowledge of the target users' hardware and software environment. These infrastructure experts provide the practical knowledge of the day-to-day computer system operation into which new technologies must fit, as well as the approval processes that a new software program must pass through before being permitted to operate on a user's computer.

Through partnerships with the IT infrastructure staff, software can be hardened and customized to meet the needs of the environment. Before the software can be provided to users, however, a support infrastructure must be put into place to provide users with initial training as well as ongoing support and consultation. This requires partnerships with training and user support organizations as well as the user organizations.

Sophisticated new technologies can be literally disruptive to the user's working environment. This can have both positive and negative connotations. In the positive sense, the new tools can change the work for the better, streamlining processes and enabling fundamentally new and different analyses that were not previously possible. On the other hand, new tools disrupt the user's familiar, comfortable working patterns. New tools require the user to not only learn the mechanics of the tools but also how to adapt his or her processes to best take advantage of the tools' new capabilities.

Consequently, training and user support play a critical role. Training must take into account the fact that in pressure-filled environments, where time is at a premium, users generally do not have the luxury of time to explore and experiment with new tools. Training must be concise and focused. First and foremost, users must understand how a new tool applies to their tasks and processes and what new capabilities it provides them. The focus should be on the process first, and then the mechanics of using the tool. Ideally, users should be able to learn to use a new tool by applying it to an existing task.

Training classes alone cannot provide a user with complete proficiency in using a new tool. Instead, the users must have access to individuals that understand both the software and the analytical process. These expert consultants must be available for questions, but they also provide value by conducting a proactive follow-up with users to identify and help overcome hurdles in using the tools.

Technology insertion is a gradual process. Ideally, new tools will be rolled out slowly, with a few early adopters providing valuable insights about how well new tools meet analytical needs. The feedback from these early users is critical to shaping the ongoing growth and evolution of the analytical tools. These users, too, can provide additional support to their workgroups as more and more people adopt the tools.

Recommendation 6.10

In coordination with the appropriate government information technology infrastructure support organizations, develop a strategy for insertion of new and promising visual analytics technologies into operational use.

Our goal is to help remove barriers associated with successful adoption of visual analytics technology so that users can derive optimal benefit from these new capabilities. An important first step is to identify best practices for technology insertion by examining examples of successful technology insertion activities. These practices can be shared and refined to create processes for transferring state-of-the-art visual analytic technologies into the operational environment quickly and comprehensively.

Summary

The issues associated with moving research into practice are often omitted from R&D agendas of this type. However, this panel felt compelled to provide a framework for fundamental issues associated with accelerating the process of getting technology into the hands of users. Each of these issues has the potential to make or break the successful deployment of the new technologies we are recommending.

Summary Recommendations

The following high-level recommendations summarize the detailed recommendations from this chapter. These actions are necessary to accelerate the transition of research into practice.

Recommendation

Develop an infrastructure to facilitate evaluation of new visual analytics technologies.

All too often we develop and deploy technology that has not been evaluated within the contexts of its intended use. This is especially true when dealing with the bridge between unclassified and classified applications. We need common methods and measures for evaluation, with a focus not only on performance but also on utility.

Evaluation is an iterative process that will require a support infrastructure in order to succeed. It begins with evaluations of research done by the inventors themselves. Good sources of unclassified test data will be required to support this evaluation. The most promising research will mature through further stages of development and refinement and will be combined with other technologies, with progressively more sophisticated evaluations conducted in unclassified visual analytics test beds that will be established to approximate the target deployment environment. Conducting these evaluations will require a test bed infrastructure with more representative, but still unclassified, test data streams to use for evaluation. Ultimately, tools will be evaluated in technology insertion facilities that directly replicate the target production environments, which will require close collaboration among government and research communities. The lessons learned throughout the evaluation process should be captured from this process and shared throughout the community.

Recommendation

Create and use a common security and privacy infrastructure, with support for incorporating privacy-supporting technologies, such as data minimization and data anonymization.

The goal of visual analytics R&D is to create fundamentally new ways for people to understand and act upon the data available to them. However, this must be done within a framework that fully considers and supports the need for privacy in all phases of the work, from the earliest research stages to the deployment phase.

To make attention to privacy a natural and routine part of the visual analytics R&D process, we need to adopt a standard suite of anonymization technologies and make these available to the visual analytics research community. We further recommend that all researchers in visual analytics receive training so that they clearly understand privacy and security laws and policies and do not inadvertently invent technologies or use data that violate privacy laws and policies.

Recommendation

Use a common component-based software development approach for visual analytics software to facilitate evaluation of research results in integrated prototypes and deployment of promising components in diverse operational environments.

Software interoperability is important to the visual analytics R&D effort. Initially, complementary technologies created by different research teams will be evaluated together in test beds to determine how best to deploy them. Ultimately, though, the most promising breakthrough technologies are likely to have broad applicability and thus will be candidates for deployment into diverse analyst-focused systems in use within DHS and other government agencies. The only effective path to rapid and cost-effective deployment of new technologies is to develop them in the form of reusable software components.

Recommendation

Identify and publicize best practices for inserting visual analytics technologies into operational environments.

One measure of success for this R&D agenda is the extent to which the resulting research matures into software that finds broad usage. The process of transitioning software into broad analytical use is complex, and it requires the cooperative efforts of researchers, software engineers, systems infrastructure and operations staff, training and support staff, and the users themselves. Although the process can be difficult, there are examples of successful transitions that provide important lessons and guideposts for future technology insertion efforts. By identifying and publicizing these best practices, we can help speed the transition of the next generation of innovative research into the user's hands.

References

Agrawal R, J Kiernan, R Srikant, and Y Xu. 2002. "Hippocratic Databases." In *Proceedings of the 28th International Conference of Very Large Databases*, pp. 143-154. Hong Kong, China. Morgan Kaufmann, San Francisco. Available at http://www.cs.ust.hk/vldb2002/ vldb2002/.

Alonso D, A Rose, C Plaisant, and K Norman. 1998 "Viewing Personal History Records: A Comparison of Tabular Format and Graphical Presentation Using LifeLines." *Behavior and Information Technology* 17(5):249-262.

Chen C and E Yu. 2000. "Empirical Studies of Information Visualization: A Meta-Analysis." *International Journal of Human-Computer Studies* 53(5):851-866.

Chinchor N, D Lewis, and L Hirschman. 1993. "Evaluating Message Understanding Systems: An Analysis of the Third Message Understanding Conference (MUC-3)." *Computational Linguistics* 19(3):409-449.

Committee on National Security Systems. 2003. *National Information Assurance (IA) Glossary*, CNSS Instruction No. 4009.

Cowley P, L Nowell, and J Scholtz. 2005. "Glass Box: An Instrumented Infrastructure for Supporting Human-Interaction with Information." In *Proceedings of the Thirty-Eighth Annual Hawaii International Conference on System Sciences*, January 3-6, 2005. Available at http://csdl.computer. org/comp/proceedings/hicss/2005/2268/09/22680296c.pdf.

Dempsey J and P Rosenzweig. 2004. "Technologies That Can Protect Privacy as Information is Shared to Combat Terrorism." *The Heritage Foundation*. Available at http://www.heritage.org/ Research/HomelandDefense/lm11.cfm.

Department of Defense Technology and Privacy Advisory Committee (TAPAC). 2004. *Safeguarding Privacy in the Fight Against Terrorism*. U.S. Department of Defense, Washington, D.C.

Department of Homeland Security. 2004. *Securing our Homeland: U.S. Department of Homeland Security Strategic Plan*. Available at http://www.dhs.gov/interweb/assetlibrary/DHS_StratPlan_ FINAL_spread.pdf.

Federal Information Security Management Act (FISMA) of 2002, Pub. L. No. 107-296, Title X, § 1001, 116 Stat. 2259.

Gehrke J, P Ginsparg, and J Kleinburg. 2004. "Overview of the 2003 KDD Cup." *SIGKDD Explorations* 5(2):149-151.

Gonzales V and A Kobsa. 2003. "Benefits of Information Visualization for Administrative Data Analysts." In *Proceedings of the Seventh International Conference on Information Visualization*, pp. 331-337. London.

Grinstein G, P Hoffman, S Laskowski, and R Pickett. 2001. "Benchmark Development for the Evaluation of Visualization for Data Mining." In *Information Visualization in Data Mining and Knowledge Discovery*, pp. 129-176, eds. U Fayyad, G Grinstein, and A Wierse. Morgan Kaufmann, San Francisco.

Griswold v. Connecticut, 381 US 479, 1965.

Irani P and C Ware. 2003. "Diagramming Information Structures Using 3D Perceptual Primitives." *ACM Transactions on Computer-Human Interaction* 10(1):1-19.

Kobsa A. 2004. "User Experiments with Tree Visualization Systems." In *Proceedings of the IEEE Symposium on Information Visualization*, pp. 9-16.

Mackinlay J. 1986. "Automating the Design of Graphical Presentations of Relational Information." *ACM Transactions on Graphics* 5(2):110-141.

Oliveira SR and R Zaiane. 2003. *Geometric Data Transformation for Privacy Preserving Clustering.* TR 03-12, Department of Computer Science, University of Alberta, Canada. Available at http://www.cs.ualberta.ca/TechReports/2003/TR03-12/TR03-12.pdf.

Pallett D, J Garofolo, and J Fiscus. 2000. "Measurement in Support of Research Accomplishments." *Communications of the ACM* 43(2):75-79.

Plaisant C. 2004. "The Challenge of Information Visualization Evaluation." *Proceedings of the Working Conference on Advanced Visual Interfaces*, pp. 109-116. ACM Press, New York.

Plaisant C, J Fekete, and G Grinstein. 2004. *Promoting Insight Based Evaluation of Information Visualization: From Contests to Benchmark Repository.* Technical Report 2004-30, Human-Computer Interaction Laboratory, University of Maryland, College Park, Maryland.

Plaisant C, J Grosjean, and BB Bederson. 2002. "SpaceTree: Supporting Exploration in Large Node-Link Tree: Design Evolution and Empirical Evaluation." 2002. In *Proceedings of the IEEE Symposium on Information Visualization*, pp. 57-64. IEEE Computer Society, Washington, D.C.

Privacy Act of 1974, Pub. L. No. 93-579, 88 Stat. 1896.

Saraiya P, C North, and K Duca. 2004. "An Evaluation of Microarray Visualization Tools for Biological Insight." In *Proceedings of IEEE Symposium on Information Visualization*, pp. 1-8. IEEE Computer Society, Washington, D.C.

Stasko J, R Catrambone, M Guzdial, and K McDonald. 2000. "An Evaluation of Space-Filling Information Visualizations for Depicting Hierarchical Structures." *International Journal of Human-Computer Studies* 53(5):663-694.

Steves MP and J Scholtz. 2005. "A Framework for Evaluating Collaborative Systems in the Real World." In *Proceedings of the Thirty-Eighth Annual Hawaii International Conference on System Sciences*, January 3-6, Computer Society Press, Washington, D.C.

Trafton J, T Tsui, R Miyamoto, J Ballas, and P Raymond. 2000. "Turning Pictures into Numbers: Extracting and Generating Information from Complex Visualizations." *International Journal of Human Computer Studies* 53(5):827-850.

Voorhees E and D Harman.2000. "Overview of the Sixth Text Retrieval Conference (TREC-6)." *Information Processing and Management* 36:3-35.

"Strong reasons make strong actions."
—William Shakespeare (1564-1616), *The Life and Death of King John*

Positioning for Enduring Success

The research and development (R&D) agenda for visual analytics constitutes a grand challenge for the scientific enterprise, but achieving this agenda is vital to the mission to protect our homeland. The scale, diversity, and complexity of available information pose both challenges and opportunities throughout the analytical process. To address this complexity and its associated uncertainty will require advances in the science of analytical reasoning. The mind must be enabled to provide better judgment through new visual representations and interaction techniques. These techniques must be supported by advanced data transformations and representations. Diverse data must be brought together, or synthesized, to enable the detection of the expected and discovery of the unexpected. Often forgotten is the requirement for new methods to effectively communicate analytical understandings to a wide variety of users to enable further action. The combination of all of these requirements constitutes a grand scientific challenge.

This agenda is likely to take 5 to 10 years to fully address. Its achievement requires the establishment and continual enhancement of tool suites that are evaluated to prove effectiveness and utility. These tools must be engineered to support security and privacy policies. They must be developed with an understanding that they will be deployed in a wide variety of environments.

Achievement of this agenda also requires the development of educational foundations to stimulate a new generation of scientists and engineers. Although rapid incremental advancements can be made by delivering interim software suites, significant investments are necessary to establish educational partnerships and programs that engage the best talents possible in building the capability to fully achieve this mission. These investments are essential to positioning the science for enduring success.

The recommendations presented in Chapters 2–6 will enable researchers to make major breakthroughs in discovering and creating new technologies that enable profound insights from massive and dynamic data. These technologies will facilitate new understanding that can be used to protect against terrorist attacks, secure our borders, and assist in timely response in the event of an attack or other major emergency. The urgency of protecting our homeland demands strong leadership to achieve this science and technology mission and to develop an enduring multidisciplinary community of practice to meet these needs. The resulting capabilities will also have a broad impact on other disciplines where data-intensive analytics are required, such as biology and medicine.

This chapter addresses the critical foundational elements that are necessary to achieve the R&D agenda described in this book. It discusses the urgency of accomplishing this agenda; it addresses the need for partnerships and collaboration; and it outlines the need for funding and coordination. It concludes with our recommendations and a call to action.

Urgency of the Visual Analytics Mission

It is fair to ask: Why now? For the family members of those lost to terrorism, we are already late. Examinations of the events leading to terrorist attacks have produced calls for new processes, methods, and technologies to prevent, protect, and respond to future threats. We cannot delay.

This agenda must be accomplished expeditiously. This agenda calls for *accelerated creation of new capabilities* and streamlining their evaluation and implementation so that they may have a direct and transforming impact on the day-to-day activities of protecting the country. If new research is conducted and papers are published but no new tools are placed in users' hands, our goals will not be met. To achieve success, we must adopt a *science-to-solutions* approach to address the entire research, development, and deployment process. We must create a close partnership between the researchers discovering new approaches and the engineers who are putting those methods into practice. New and important research challenges come to light when putting technology into practice. To ensure that these emerging challenges are identified and addressed rapidly, a strong connection among research, engineering, and technology insertion is essential.

Technical success will require experts in many sciences working together to understand the challenges, develop high-impact technologies, and learn from evaluations to rapidly develop and deploy the required capabilities. We must engage experts in mathematics, statistics, cognitive and perceptual sciences, knowledge discovery and engineering, visualization, and many other sub-disciplines within computer science, as well as experts in reasoning and decision sciences, communications, graphics design, and other related disciplines. Multidisciplinary teams must work together to jointly understand the technical challenges and develop common taxonomies with which they can communicate. These shared foundations must be put in place to allow teams to invent, develop, and evaluate technology that is quickly adopted within targeted mission areas. We recommend that users, to the extent possible, be involved from the start in order to provide insight and grounding to the teams.

An important goal is to provide an enduring capability in which growing teams of experts throughout the research and engineering communities remain focused on the creation of new, high-impact technologies for visual analytics. With the overwhelming volume of data rapidly increasing, we will continue, for the foreseeable future, to collect more data than we can effectively analyze within time and mission constraints. While we grow in our abilities to detect, prevent, and respond to terrorist attacks, the potential attackers will become increasingly sophisticated. This means that we must continue to advance our technologies to meet ever-growing needs.

To create this enduring capability, our educational enterprise must be engaged from the start. We need a new multidisciplinary curriculum to prepare new researchers for careers in visual analytics R&D. Students must have opportunities to augment their education with internships at national laboratories and other applied research locations to see the context of the technical challenges firsthand. Faculty should have opportunities to spend extended periods of time in national laboratories or industry supporting this mission. One example of an existing program to address this need is the US Department of Homeland Security (DHS) Scholars and Fellows Program. We must assist universities in understanding user needs through access to speakers and training, and we must provide support for transforming innovative technology demonstrations into robust software tools that can be deployed in the homeland security user community.

In summary, successfully accomplishing this agenda will demand more than the achievement of individual technical recommendations. It requires the involvement of the users and an understanding of their analytical processes. It requires the formation of multidisciplinary teams that can rapidly translate this understanding into innovative software suites. It demands a continuous cycle of research, engineering, evaluation, and technology insertion. It requires a concerted effort on the part of a diverse group of scientists and engineers working in partnership, and it can be sustained over the long term only through an active focus on education.

Meeting the Challenges through Partnerships and Collaborations

Accomplishing this R&D agenda will require the efforts of teams of researchers throughout academia, industry, and the national laboratory system. However, it will not be sufficient to have these research teams working in isolation on parts of this grand challenge.

Instead, we must establish a community of practice for visual analytics research and engineering. This community of practice will be an important source of information for the researchers and engineers about user needs. The community of practice must foster appropriate collaborations with user organizations both to inform new research directions and to evaluate promising research. It must bring together the entire research community to support information sharing and collaboration. In addition, it must support collaboration among funding agencies to enable the most efficient use of investments.

While DHS will provide initial leadership establishing these partnerships and collaborations, it will ultimately be up to the R&D institutions to work in concert to build an enduring community of practice in visual analytics.

Funding and Coordination

Visual analytics R&D efforts must be coordinated to achieve the highest possible return on research investments. Elements of the R&D agenda are being funded at varying levels by several government agencies. Researchers and engineers must be made aware of the technical advances being made in these areas, and government agencies must be able to stay abreast of what others are funding.

Technical forums should be held to share advancing technologies. These should leverage existing technical meetings such as those sponsored by the Institute of Electrical and Electronics Engineers, Inc. (IEEE) and Association of Computing Machinery (ACM) to the extent possible to maximize the information sharing while minimizing the number of schedule disruptions that the researchers must accommodate. Special-purpose conferences and workshops will also be needed to allow focused attention to areas of particular interest.

The challenge of funding this R&D agenda must be addressed. This agenda will not be accomplished through small, isolated investment programs. The necessary investments will not likely be developed through one agency, one company, or one national laboratory but through a coordinated, or at least confederated, suite of investments. The investments must address a full suite of needs including basic research, applied research, testing and evaluation, product engineering, and technology insertion and training. In one possible model, individual government agencies choose to invest in portions of the R&D agenda that have the most direct impact on their work. Industry researchers can focus on portions of the agenda for which they see the most potential commercial applications. The National Visualization and Analytics Center™ (NVAC™) can serve as the focal point for awareness about the R&D agenda. NVAC can identify areas in which substantial new research is needed and communicate this to potential funders of R&D effort. In addition, NVAC can provide a forum for the visual analytics research community, the funding sponsors, and other stakeholders to share breakthroughs, emerging requirements, and plans.

Although the final model chosen may differ from the one we describe here, we believe that a successful model can be established. We are encouraged by the strong interest from academia, industry, and the national laboratories to help bring solutions to the analytic community.

A critical requirement for the success of this agenda is the government's role in stimulating this agenda, the investment programs, and the *science-to-solutions* culture for the protection of our homeland. The government must remain dedicated in its support for funding this grand challenge. The success of its investments can be measured via peer reviews, technology insertion and, most of all, the utility of these technologies to the end users. Congressional commitments are needed to fund research in visual analytics. Although the cost of this research will be substantial, the cost of failure to achieve this agenda is far greater, as it is measured in lives lost and major economic impact.

Recommendations

Achieving the agenda outlined here will require the sustained efforts of a multi-disciplinary community of researchers. Educational efforts and partnerships are necessary to establish and sustain an enduring visual analytics R&D community capable of meeting these challenges.

Recommendation 7.1

Develop programs to support education of the research community about the drivers for visual analytics research.

Two major educational efforts are required. First, we must work in conjunction with universities to influence university curricula to provide formal education about visual analytics needs and challenges. Second, we must provide an active continuing education program through workshops, tutorials, and conferences to provide a broad understanding of analytic needs, technical challenges, and state-of-the-art R&D. These forums will be open to practitioners from academia, industry, and the national laboratory system.

Recommendation 7.2

Form university-led centers of excellence and partnerships with industry, national laboratories, and selected international research entities to bring together the best talents to accomplish the visual analytics R&D agenda.

NVAC should be the coordinating point for the achievement of the visual analytics R&D agenda. University-led centers of excellence should be established to focus on advancement of specific high-priority portions of the agenda.

In addition, opportunities must be provided so that experts outside academia can contribute to advancement of this agenda. Avenues must be provided for partnerships with researchers, both individually and organizationally, in industry, in government, and in the national laboratory system. Selected international collaborations and partnerships should also be established to accomplish portions of the research mission.

Recommendation 7.3

Establish special partnerships with user organizations and the Corporate Information Office (CIO) organizations that support them to facilitate technology insertion within their operational environments.

Transitioning technology into operation is a complex challenge and requires intimate knowledge of the domain into which the technology will be deployed. Partnerships with user organizations and their supporting CIO offices can supply the necessary insight to understand the analytical needs and the operational constraints for software being deployed. These insights are essential to accelerating the process of transitioning research into operation.

Provide ongoing support for collaborations, internships, staff exchanges, educational material development, and other efforts that foster interest in R&D that addresses the missions of homeland security.

This support is a critical need to meet DHS's mission of enduring security for the homeland. This educational outreach effort should be coordinated with the DHS Educational Programs Office and stimulated by coordinated learning and training investments.

Call to Action

The agenda described herein is only a beginning. As the new discipline of visual analytics matures during the next few years, our understanding of the research challenges and priorities will grow rapidly.

To remain on target for accomplishing this agenda, we will periodically evaluate its progress. While success may be measured in many ways, we choose to focus on two specific areas for evaluation. This effort will be a success if:

- New visual analytic techniques are being successfully transitioned into practice
- A vibrant and growing community of practice has been established for visual analytics researchers and engineers.

This R&D agenda constitutes a grand challenge. While DHS is providing the foundational support for this effort, its success must be realized through the coordinated support and efforts of multiple government agencies, industry, academia, and the national laboratories. As we mobilize to address this challenge, we are mindful of the role we play in helping to safeguard our nation.

Additional Reading

At the conclusion of each chapter, we have included references to materials directly cited in the chapter. However, there are many additional publications relevant to aspects of visual analytics, some of which are listed here for further reading.

Ankerst M, S Berchtold, and D Keim. 1998. "Similarity Clustering of Dimensions for an Enhanced Visualization of Multidimensional Data." In *Proceedings of the 1998 IEEE Symposium on Information Visualization (InfoVis 98)*, pp. 52-60. IEEE Computer Society, Washington, D.C.

Bolt RA. 1984. *The Human Interface*. Lifetime Learning Publications, Belmont, California.

Bolt RA. 1987. "Conversing with Computers." In *Readings in Human-Computer Interaction: A Multidisciplinary Approach*, eds. RM Braeker and AS Buxton. Morgan Kaufmann Publishers, Inc., Los Altos, California.

Breiman L. 1984. *Classification and Regression Trees*. Kluwer Academic, Boston.

Breiman L. 2001. "Random Forests." *Machine Learning* 45(1):5-32.

Brodbeck D, M Chalmers, A Lunzer, and P Cotture. 1997. "Domesticating Bead: Adapting an Information Visualization System to a Financial Institution." In *Proceedings of the 1997 IEEE Symposium on Information Visualization (InfoVis 97)*, pp. 73-80. IEEE Computer Society, Washington, D.C.

Buneman P, S Davidson, M Liberman, C Overton, and V Tannen. 1998. *Data Provenance*. Available at http://www.cis.upenn.edu/~wctan/DataProvenance/prov.html.

Carroll J, MB Rosson, D Dunlap, and P Isenhour. 2003. "Frameworks for Sharing Knowledge Toward a Professional Language for Teaching Practices." In *Proceedings of the 36th Hawaii International Conference on System Sciences*, pp. 120-129. IEEE Computer Society, Washington, D.C.

Carroll JM, DC Neale, PL Isenhour, MB Rosson, and DS McCrickard. 2003. "Notification and Awareness: Synchronizing Task-Oriented Collaborative Activity." *International Journal of Human-Computer Systems* 58(5):605-632.

Czerwinski M, G Smith, T Regan, B Meyers, G Robertson, and G Starkweather. 2003. "Toward Characterizing the Productivity Benefits of Very Large Displays." In *Human-Computer Interaction-INTERACT 2003*, eds. M Rauterberg, M Menozzi, and J Wesson, pp. 252-255. IOS Press, copyright IFIP.

Davidson I and M Ward. 2001. "A Particle Visualization Framework for Clustering and Anomaly Detection." In *Proceedings of the ACM KDD Workshop on Visual Data Mining*. Available at http://www.inf.uni-konstanz.de/~keim/KDD_Workshop/KDD_Proceeding.pdf.

de Silva V and G Carlsson. 2004. "Topological Estimation Using Witness Complexes." In *Proceedings of the Eurographics Symposium on Point-Based Graphics*, pp. 157-166.

Derthick M, M Christel, A Hauptmann, and H Wactlar. 2003. "Constant Density Displays Using Diversity Sampling." In *Proceedings of Information Visualization 2003*, pp. 137-144.

Domingos P and G Hulten. 2003. "A General Framework for Mining Massive Data Streams." *Journal of Computational & Graphical Statistics* 12(4):945-949.

Dufner D, O Kwon, and R Hadidi. 1999. "Web-CCAT: A Collaborative Learning Environment for Geographically Distributed Information for Technology Students and Working Professionals." *Communications of the Association for Information Systems* (1)12.

Ekman P and M O'Sullivan. 1991. "Who Can Catch a Liar?" *American Psychologist* 46: 913-920.

Fitzmaurice G and W Buxton. 1997. "An Empirical Evaluation of Graspable User Interfaces: Towards Specialized, Space-Multiplexed Input." In *Proceedings of the ACM Conference on Human Factors in Computing Systems (CHI'97)*, pp. 43-50. ACM Press, New York.

Fua Y, M Ward, and E Rundensteiner. 1999. "Hierarchical Parallel Coordinates for Exploration of Large Data Sets." In *Proceedings of the Conference on Visualization '99: Celebrating Ten Years*, pp. 43-50. IEEE Computer Society Press, Los Alamitos, California.

Garbis C. 2002. "Exploring the Openness of Cognitive Artifacts in Cooperative Process Management." *Cognition, Technology & Work* 4(1):9-21.

Gonzalez RC and RE Woods. 2002. *Digital Image Processing*. Second edition, Prentice-Hall, Englewood Cliffs, New Jersey.

Grudin J. 2001. "Partitioning Digital Worlds: Focal and Peripheral Awareness in Multiple Monitor Use." In *Proceedings of SIGCHI Conference on Human Factors in Computing Systems*, pp. 458-465. ACM Press, New York.

Guarino N. 1997. "Understanding, Building and Using Ontologies." *International Journal of Human-Computer Studies* 46(2/3):293-310.

Guimbretiere F, M Stone, and T Winograd. 2001. "Fluid Interaction with High-Resolution Wall-Size Displays." In *Proceedings of the 14th Annual Symposium on User Interface Software Technology*, pp. 21-30. ACM Press, New York.

Healey CG, KS Booth, and JT Enns. 1993. "Harnessing Preattentive Processes for Multivariate Data Visualization." In *Proceedings of Graphics Interface '93, pp. 107-117*. Toronto, Canada.

Hedges LV and I Olkin. 1985. *Statistical Methods for Meta-Analysis*. Academic Press, New York.

Hiltz SR, D Dufner, M Holmes, and MS Poole. 1991. "Distributed Group Support Systems: Social Dynamics and Design Dilemmas." *Journal of Organizational Computing* 2(1):135-159.

Höllerer T, S Feiner, D Hallaway, B Bell, M Lanzagorta, D Brown, S Julier, Y Baillot, and L Rosenblum. "User Interface Management Techniques for Collaborative Mobile Augmented Reality." *Computers & Graphics* 25(5):799-810.

Ishii H and B Ullmer. 1997. "Tangible Bits: Towards Seamless Interfaces Between People, Bits and Atoms." In *Proceedings of the SIGCHI Conference on Human Factors in Computing Systems*, pp. 234-241, Atlanta, Georgia. ACM Press, New York.

Johanson B, A Fox, and T Winograd. 2002. "The Interactive Workspaces Project: Experiences with Ubiquitous Computing Rooms." *IEEE Pervasive Computing Magazine* 1(2):67-74.

Julier S, M Lanzagorta, Y Baillot, and D Brown. 2002. "Information Filtering for Mobile Augmented Reality, Projects in VR." *IEEE Computer Graphics & Applications* 22(5):12-15.

Julier S, MA Livingston, JE Swan II, Y Baillot, and D Brown. 2003. "Adaptive User Interfaces in Augmented Reality." Presented at *Proceedings of the 2nd International Symposium on Mixed and Augmented Reality (STARS 2003)*, Tokyo, Japan.

Kay P. 1993. "Speech Driven Graphics: a User Interface." *Journal of Microcomputer Applications* 16:223-231.

Koren Y and L Carmel. 2003. "Visualization of Labeled Data Using Linear Transformations." In *Proceedings of the IEEE Symposium on Information Visualization (InfoVis 03)*, pp. 121-128. IEEE Computer Society Press, Los Alamitos, California.

Kress G and T van Leeuwen. 1998. *Reading Images: The Grammar of Visual Design*. Routledge, London.

Lee AB, KS Pedersen, and D Mumford. 2003. "The Nonlinear Statistics of High-Contrast Patches in Natural Images." *International Journal of Computer Vision* 54(1-3):83-103.

Lu A, C Morris, J Taylor, DS Ebert, P Rheingans, C Hansen, and M Hartner. 2003. "Illustrative Interactive Stipple Rendering." *IEEE Transactions on Visualization and Computer Graphics* 9(2):127-139.

Lum EB and K Ma. 2002. "Hardware-Accelerated Parallel Non-Photorealistic Volume Rendering." In *Proceedings of the 2nd International Symposium on Non-Photorealistic Animation and Rendering*, pp. 67-74. ACM Press, New York.

Mitchell T. 1997. *Machine Learning*. McGraw-Hill, New York.

Morrison A, G Ross, and M Chalmers. 2003. "Fast Multidimensional Scaling Through Sampling, Springs, and Interpolation." *Information Visualization* 2:68-77.

Oviatt SL, PR Cohen, L Wu, J Vergo, L Duncan, B Suhm, J Bers, T Holzman, T Winograd, J Landay, J Larson, and D Ferro. 2000. "Designing the User Interface for Multimodal Speech and Pen-Based Gesture Applications: State-of-the-Art Systems and Future Research Directions." *Human-Computer Interaction* 15(4):263-322.

Piekarski W and BH Thomas. 2002. *Unifying Augmented Reality and Virtual Reality User Interfaces*, Technical Report, University of South Australia, Adelaide, South Australia.

Piekarski W and B Thomas. 2003. "Augmented Reality User Interfaces and Techniques for Outdoor Modelling." In *Proceedings of the 2003 Symposium on Interactive 3D Graphics*, pp. 225-226. ACM Press, New York.

Roberts L. 1963. *Machine Perception of 3D Solids*, Ph.D. Dissertation, MIT Department of Electrical Engineering, Cambridge, Massachusetts.

Rosario G, E Rundensteiner, D Brown, and M Ward. 2004. "Mapping Nominal Values to Numbers for Effective Visualization." In *Information Visualization: Special Issue of Selected and Extended InfoVis 03 Papers* 3(2):80-95. Palgrave Macmillan, Basingstoke, New York.

Salisbury MW, JH Hendrickson, TL Lammers, C Fu, and SA Moody. 1990. "Talk and Draw: Bundling Speech and Graphics." *Computer* 23(8):59-65.

Schum D. 1987. *Evidence and Inference for the Intelligence Analyst*. University Press of America, Lanham, Maryland.

Stefik M, G Foster, D Bobrow, K Kahn, S Lanning, and L Suchman. 1987. "Beyond the Chalkboard: Computer Support for Collaboration and Problem Solving in Meetings." *Communications of the ACM* 30(1):32-47.

Stevens SS. 1946. "On the Theory of Scales of Measurement." *Science* 103:677-680.

Stewart J, B Bederson, and A Druin. 1999. "Single Display Groupware: A Model for Co-Present Collaboration." In *Proceedings of Human Factors in Computing Systems (CHI 99)*, pp. 286-293. ACM Press, Pittsburgh, Pennsylvania.

Streitz NA, J Geißler, and T Holmer. 1998. "Roomware® for Cooperative Buildings: Integrated Design of Architectural Spaces and Information Spaces." In *Proceedings of the First International Workshop on Cooperative Buildings*, pp. 4-21, Darmstadt, Germany. Springer-Verlag, Heidelberg, Germany.

Studeny M and J Vejnarova. 1988. "The MultiInformation Function as a Tool for Measuring Stochastic Dependence." In *Learning in Graphical Models*, MI Jordan, ed., pp. 261-297. Kluwer Academic, Boston.

Tang D, C Stolte, and R Bosch. 2004. "Design Choices When Architecting Visualizations." In *Information Visualization: Special Issue of Selected and Extended InfoVis 03 Papers*, pp. 65-79.

Treavett SMF and M Chen. 2000. "Pen-and-Ink Rendering in Volume Visualisation." In *Proceedings of the Conference on Visualization '00*, p. 203-210, Salt Lake City, Utah. IEEE, Piscataway, New Jersey.

Tversky B. 1993. "Cognitive Maps, Cognitive Collages and Spatial Mental Models." In *Spatial Information Theory – A Theoretical Basis for GIS, Proceedings of the European Conference COSIT '93*, pp. 14-24. Springer-Verlag, Elba.

van Dam A, V Abrash, O Bernsen, T Furness, B Herzog, T Kunii, B Shneiderman, M Turk, and T Whitted. 1999. "Report of the Working Group on Foundations of Future Interfaces: Devices, Hardware and Software." In *Special Report on Human Centered Computing, Online Communities and Virtual Environments* ACM SIGGRAPH 33(3):49-54.

Weiser M. 1991. "The Computer for the Twenty-First Century." *Scientific American* 265(3):94-104.

Wellner P. 1993. "Interactions with Paper on the Digital Desk." *Communications of the ACM* 36(7):87-96.

Wills G. 1998. "An Interactive View for Hierarchical Clustering." In *Proceedings of the 1998 IEEE Symposium on Information Visualization*, pp. 26-31. IEEE Computer Society, Washington, D.C.

Wise J, J Thomas, K Pennock, D Lantrip, M Pottier, A Schur, and V Crow. 1995. "Visualizing the Non-Visual: Spatial Analysis and Interaction with Information from Text Documents." In *Proceedings of Information Visualization '95*, pp. 51-58. IEEE Computer Society Press, Los Alamitos, California.

Wong P, P Whitney, and J Thomas. 1999. "Visualizing Association Rules for Text Mining." In *Proceedings of the 1999 IEEE Symposium on Information Visualization*, pp. 120-123. IEEE Computer Society, Washington, D.C.

Woodruff A and M Stonebraker. 1997. "Supporting Fine-Grained Data Lineage in a Database Visualization Environment." In *Proceedings of the International Conference on Data Engineering*, pp. 91-102.

Acronyms

ACM	Association of Computing Machinery
AES	Advanced Encryption Standard
AGS	Association Grounded Semantics
ANN	artificial neural network
API	application programming interface
APT	Automated Presentation Tool
AQUAINT	Advanced Question and Answering for Intelligence
ARDA	Advanced Research and Development Activity
CHI	Computer-Human Interaction
CIA	Central Intelligence Agency
CIO	Corporate Information Office
CPOF	Command Post of the Future
CRT	Cathode Ray Tube
CSCW	Computer Supported Collaborative Work
CUSUM	cumulative sum
DARPA	Defense Advanced Research Projects Agency
DHS	Department of Homeland Security
DoS	Denial of Service
DSS	Digital Signature Standard
EARS	Effective, Affordable, Reusable Speech-to-Text
EOS	Earth Observation Satellite
FIPS	Federal Information Processing Standard
FISMA	Federal Information Security Management Act
GIS	geographic information system
GITI	Global Information and Telecommunication Institute
GO	gene ontologies
GPS	Global Positioning System
HMAC	Hash Message Authentication Code
IBM	International Business Machines Corporation
IEEE	Institute of Electrical and Electronics Engineers
I/O	input/output
ISOMAP	Isometric Mapping
IT	information technology
JPL	Jet Propulsion Laboratory

KDD	Knowledge Discovery and Data Mining
LCD	Liquid Crystal Display
LCOS	Liquid Crystal on Silicon
LDA	latent Dirichlet allocation
LLE	Local Linear Embeddings
LSI	Latent Semantic Indexing
MDS	Multi-Dimensional Scaling
MUC	Message Understand Conference
NASA	National Aeronautics and Space Administration
NER	named entity recognition
NIAP	National Information Assurance Partnership
NIST	National Institute of Standards and Technology
NLP	natural language processing
NVAC	National Visualization and Analytics Center
OLAP	online analytical processing
OLED	Organic Light-Emitting Diode
PDA	personal digital assistant
PLSI	Probabilistic Latent Semantic Indexing
RBAC	role-based access control
R&D	research and development
RDBMS	relational database management system
RSS	remote syndication services
SDDS	Scientific Discovery through Dual Search
SID	System for Information Discovery
SIGGRAPH	Special Interest Group on Graphical Displays
SVD	singular value decomposition
TAPAC	Technology and Privacy Advisory Committee
TREC	Text REtrieval Conference
UTM	Universal Transverse Mercator
VHD	very-high-dimensional
VNC	Virtual Network Computing